IMAGES OF A NIC

FLORENCE NIGHTINGALE

IMAGES
of a
NIGHTINGALE

Susan Coventry

Beuclerk 1992

First published in 1990 by
Beauclerk Publishing
29 The Gilberts, Sea Road
Rustington, West Sussex

7th Reprint April 1993
(Also in hardback)

ISBN 0-9516505-1-3

Cover print of Florence Nightingale:
Mary Evans Picture Library
Cover sketch by Caspar Reid

Acknowlegements: quotations from:
Testament of Youth (Victor Gollancz, 1933)
and *The Unfair Sex* (William Clowes & Sons, 1953)

Printed on environmentally paper by
Booksprint, London N6 5AH

To Peggy with fondest memories

PREFACE

Nurses who train in the Nightingale Training School for Nurses at St Thomas's Hospital, London, which was founded by Florence Nightingale in the last century, are traditionally called Nightingales and, as such, they remain. When they leave the hospital they are still just Nightingales. The prefix 'old' is not attached to them as it is to many ex-pupils of schools, and yet in other ways the system is similar. To have trained at St Thomas's and to be a Nightingale creates its own form of 'old girl network'.

If one is travelling around and meets a Nightingale, immediately there is a bond. Reminiscences pour forth. There is an instinctive feeling of fusion—a contact that belies anything that could be called affinity in any other way. Definitions are sometimes hard to make exact but one could say that, for most of us, the moulding we had in the flower of our youth by the Nightingale Training School has left indelible marks on our characters that are far more deeply ingrained than by the average institution.

I am one of this race of nurses that was hewn from the Nightingale marble and, therefore, a Nightingale. I did not continue nursing after I left the hospital and am quite out of touch with the nursing world now, and yet I still consider myself a Nightingale.

How I became one is the content of my book.

1

I first saw St Thomas's Hospital whilst standing under Big Ben
looking across a radiant and reflective Thames. It stood, lightly
veiled in morning mists, with pairs of barges threaded like
moonstones along its water frontage.
St Thomas's looked that day as handsome as I ever saw it look.
Its five remaining pavilion blocks reached out towards the Embankment, with its lacy trimmings of plane trees and lamp posts,
like the paws of some great beast basking in milky beads of sunshine. It was not a beautiful hospital but symmetry and distinction
it had even after the wartime bombing that had become like a
healed wound on its side. In the fifties, on that first memorable day
that I saw it, it still looked proud and complete with its colonnade
stretching along its front and its roofs topped with domed and
pyramid-capped turrets. It looked the epitome of a long settled institution and housed the oldest established training school for nurses in England. And that was the reason I had come to see it.
  With little difficulty I found my way to matron's office for my interview. I was suitably dressed for the occasion. A green swagger
coat hung from huge shoulder pads and swayed almost to my
ankles so whatever was the shape of my youthful figure, she would
never have known about it. I wore a hat, too, tightly squeezing my
permed curls, and in my bag I clutched my gloves and credentials.
I had been warned that only one in eight were accepted into the
Nightingale Training School but felt that, at least, I had come well
prepared.
  I did not have long to wait before being signalled into matron's office. It was a large, rather dark room, quiet as a church and had a
suspension of something like holiness built into its atmosphere.
Matron greeted me kindly and looked immaculately sculptured in
her navy blue dress as she sat opposite me across a desk. She
started to ask me, softly, a number of penetrating questions to
which I was able to give satisfactory replies. She did not mention

the word vocation so I did not have to tell her that I had no conscious vocation for nursing at all. That the only career I had ever wanted was to be a ballet dancer but, after early promise, various accidents of fate had prevented it. That I had found my way to St Thomas's because a cousin of mine was happily working there. For all this was true.

In those days the openings for women were limited to a handful of choices. I was not in the upper academic echelons with the various careers this might have made possible. I had no gift with children either to care for or to train them. I could not have imagined myself cooped up in an office. And everything else was too risky, too vague or a man's domain.

My reasons for choosing nursing were a strange mixture of negative ones. I wanted to come to London. I wanted a training that would, as David Copperfield put it, 'not lie too heavy on the purse', since my parents had just spent a considerable sum of money on my education both in England and abroad. And, in a way, I wanted to please my mother who, I think, would have made a natural nurse, as I could not please myself. However, it would hardly have been prudent to have presented these facts to matron and, besides, I felt a genuine keenness and must have shown this as by the time my interview was over I knew I was accepted. Feeling very pleased with the outcome, I wandered round the hospital to explore the surroundings.

What I had expected, I do not know. I had never been into a hospital before and could not imagine that St Thomas's would bear any resemblance to the gleaming, anonymous corridors of those I had seen in films and, of course, it didn't. It appeared as though it had been conceived along the lines of a palace in its architecture and design. A palace that was not quite English with its Fareham brick and stone dressings. In its original state, as designed by Henry Currey, there had been six ward pavilion blocks that were joined at the centre by the chapel block. The whole of which was seamed along the back with corridors and along the front with a double colonnade of pillars that were mounted by a balustrade. Behind this, in between the blocks, were courtyards neatly paved and lawned. The war had changed some of this.

The most northerly block had been destroyed and buildings had mushroomed in the courtyards and there was a stricture in the main corridor where a bomb had come through the roof. But little of the other damage seemed visible and I felt the general impression must be much the same as it once had been. The remaining blocks sat solidly overlooking the Thames, with balconies along their ward fronts, elaborately moulded with ornate, almost Eastern style adornments at the horn points of their roof heads. A long terrace along Albert Embankment at its river front was raised above the thoroughfare of the wandering public.

Inside the hospital, the main artery passage of the building swept along a distance that must have been at least half of that between Westminster and Lambeth Bridges, and appeared broad enough for chariots to race along. The central hall, with its massive statue of Queen Victoria, had pillars to either side and a handsome staircase with attractively designed wrought-iron banisters. Just off the main passage, the rear staircases twined like snakes round the wells of the old fashioned lift shafts and the whole affair seemed to be spread over a huge acreage.

Vera Brittain, in her book *Testament of Youth,* deplored the immensity of the hospital in her thinly veiled descriptions of it under the pseudonym St Judes, 'those uninviting acres of brown brick with their Victorian elaborations of worn grey stone', she railed against it when describing a period she had worked there in 1918 which had not been a success. "All hope abandon ye who enter here" might have appropriately been written above its grim, gloomy doors', she continued.

Were the doors gloomy? I can't remember that I noticed but St Thomas's was in no way a gloomy place. In the leaflet handed to me that day the narrative runs:

'The six pavilions are planned to give the maximum of light and air, every ray of sun shine is secured for the benefit of patients and workers on the wards.'

And so it was. The ward blocks had been set a hundred and twenty five feet apart and therefore it was possible to install numerous windows so that nearly all the patients had one on either side of their beds. The idea for this unique style of architecture came from a similarly built hospital in France and for this Florence Nightingale was partly responsible. She felt it would decrease the risk of infection and allow for free ventilation. It also made the wards particularly light. The rest of the hospital was not gloomy either. The main passage was well lit by the arched windows on its Thames side and the corridor upstairs by similar windows on its Lambeth Palace Road face.

The planning of its architecture also seemed to facilitate navigation around its interior, rather than complicating it. A modern medical establishment, such as the new Charing Cross Hospital, with its arrowed instructions on every corner, leaves one bewildered by parallelograms in planning, and crossroads of indentical corridors and wall inscriptions in sometimes unintelligible medical parlance that take one round and round in circles. An old fashioned hospital—particularly one like St Thomas's that was built along a length and not round a square—had few such problems.

St Thomas's biggest disadvantage was that of distance. It was also ill-equipped with lifts, with only one for each block, and that out-of-bounds for staff and visitors—only to be used for patients and those who transported them. There was no quick route anywhere and therefore it required a great deal of walking along passages and mounting of stairs. One was also aware that there must have been some wastage of space, but it did serve exactly the purpose that Florence Nightingale had envisaged for it. And, visually, was a fitting tribute to its position.

The naming of the wards was also in character with its essence. These were, for the most part, very royal—Elizabeth, Alexandra, Beatrice, Christian, Edward, Arthur, Albert and George were amongst them, although the ward named after Queen Victoria had been bombed. Some of the outpatients departments were also attractively named instead of the usual clinic, unit or department.

There was Mothercraft for the gynaecological, ante natal and post natal clinics and Scutari, named after Florence Nightingales's famous town where she had nursed in the Crimea, which dealt with psychiatric problems.

The general bearing of the hospital was enhanced by the strategic positionings of statues of those people who had influenced it most. That of Florence Nightingale with her lamp, which had once graced a courtyard, was, in those postwar years, placed outside the dining room. The little stone statue of Edward VI, which had also once had its own courtyard, stood underneath the colonnade outside matron's office. Other statues were around to hear witness to its past and tell part of its story.

In the leaflet I had been given that day, that must have been printed before the war, St Thomas's was still considered a modern hospital. But, when I was there, the planners were already feasting their eyes on the future and another step in its long history had been planned. That history had begun in the seventh century when a small religious house of sisters stood on the site of the present Southwark Cathedral with a church dedicated to St Mary the Virgin. In 852 AD it was converted by St Swithin, Bishop of Winchester, to a collegiate for priests and within it a hospital for the poor. In 1106, another Bishop of Winchester, William Gifford, persuaded the collegiate priests to adopt the rule of St Augustine of Hippo and the church was renamed St Mary Overie Priory. Whilst Thomas à Becket was archbishop he enlarged the spital at the priory so, after his canonization in 1173, the name of the priory was changed to St Thomas's Spital.

In 1213 a disastrous fire destroyed most of the priory and the hospital was moved to the other side of the road—to the east side of Borough High Street, where the Cluniac Monastery of St Saviour allowed a piece of its land to be rented and the hospital in 1215 was staffed by Augustinian canons and nuns. Administered as a religious house, it continued its work until the dissolution of the monasteries under Henry VIII. However, so greatly was it missed that Bishop Ridley persuaded Edward VI to re-endow it and give it a charter under the title of the Royal Hospital of St Thomas the Apostle.

After this, three hundred years passed peacefully without in interruption but, in 1859, an Act was passed authorizing the formation of the Charing Cross railway from London Bridge to Waterloo and, as the line had to pass St Thomas's garden and close to the new north wing, the governors decided to sell the site and seek a new one. In 1863 negotiations were commenced for a site on the proposed Albert Embankment and the St Thomas's that I had come to that day was built. Queen Victoria laid the first stone there on 13th May 1868 and it was opened by her on the 21st day of June 1871.

In the 1950s one felt its past inherent in its atmosphere and every block of its stone and its history and traditions had been made more deeply significant when Florence Nightingale had selected the hospital for the foundation of the Nightingale Training School for nurses.

It was into that I was now enrolled.

2

I started my training with forty nine other girls on September 29th 1951 at the Manor House, Godalming which was the Preliminary Training School for Nightingales at the time. In many ways it was an auspicious beginning. The Manor House was a large, mock Tudor mansion set in the lip of a Surrey hillside. At the front the land fell away with lawns, knots of trees and a view of typical Surrey undulations. At the rear there was a gravel drive, the edges of which were canopied with an assortment of shrubs and trees which terminated in a sweeping oval in front of the main door. The air around it was as smooth and as clear as glass and scented with the rich, damp smells of autumn, with pine trees and with the long years of a maturing garden that creates scent as much as it does shape. I had always imagined Surrey as rather a crowded county, overloaded with silver birches, conifers and poplar trees and other busy verdancy—gorse, bracken and hawthorn—on an irregular sandy terrain. Yet there was a lovely feeling of space at the Manor House and it was pleasing.

The house seemed large by any standards, even after absorbing so many youthful women. As would be expected, there was a great deal of wood about its interior—the floors, the panelling on the walls and the solid, impressive staircase. In fact the wood of that house was to cause the first major drama of my nursing life when one Nightingale knocked a fire extinguisher—there were many of them placed round the house—off the wall and it started to jettison its deadly chemicals onto the priceless wood, leaving great snail trails of creamy foam on the panelling. A sister tutor picked it up and ran shouting to the nearest bathroom. That was on the very first day.

Downstairs there was a sitting room for the nurses overlooking the front of the house. It was there that we started our tentative relationships. We sat around, perched on the edge of chairs and stools in flannels and tweeds and twin sets, our hair in the page boy, kiss curl and lawn and rose bush styles of the day, a flouring of powder on our noses and our lips embossed with purple lipstick—awkward and inarticulate. All were strangers to one another and the conversation was as small as conversation can be. The next day, however, we were transformed. On went the heavy cottoned and purpled striped dresses, the starched collars and belts, the thirty denier black stockings and the men's black shoes. Thus began our welding together as a St Thomas's 'set'.

Most of us were nineteen (I was lucky enough to be accepted at eighteen as I had a 'difficult' October birthday). St Thomas's took girls between the ages of nineteen and thirty two but the majority of us were just nineteen, which was a good enough reason for us to find plenty in common with one another. I shared a bedroom with two girls whose names were next to mine in the alphabet. That room, which could have been big enough for eight girls at least, has left me with two indelible memories. The first was that one of my room-mates longed to slim so the other room-mate and myself spent much time rolling bottles of water (in those days, a slimming method) up and down those parts of her anatomy she wished to do away with—to nil effect.

The other memory was of the election night that October when Churchill was brought back to power. The slimming Nightingale and myself hung over the wireless into the recesses of the night (the other girl was German, so for obvious reasons it was of little interest to her and she went to sleep) counting the gains as they came in, in a fever of excitement. It wasn't really the politics, I had little political awareness then, it was the restitution of rights and glory to the war time leader who, in the minds of everyone I knew, had been deeply wronged. I suppose had I been to university and been prey to the normal mutations of opinion and ideal that take place there, I would not have felt as I did. But I only had my instincts, my loyalty and my fervour and felt that at last Churchill was getting his long overdue rewards. I remember my torch dimming on the pages of the newspaper as the last results of the night came in and a feeling of exultation that I have never felt about an election since. Those latter Churchillian years were to cover all the time I spent at St

Thomas's and were probably the most peaceful time I can remember since the war. With Churchill I had felt safe. However, I had probably not felt all that safe that night as the Manor House was run like a boarding school and our yelping glee could easily have brought wrath into the bedroom.

The sister in charge of the Manor House was, in every way, ideally chosen. To start with she was very good looking with curly, iron grey hair and Mediterranean blue eyes that could look at you with such penetration you felt they could X-ray your soul. This gave one both a feeling of nervousness and of relaxation. My respect for her was hinged the moment I met her. This was partly because she combined a subtle ability to extract from her pupils a rounded comprehension of the matter in hand without a trace of ill humour—although the way the lights changed in her eyes often made me wonder what went on behind them—and with a great deal of wit, and partly because she was such an astute judge of pace, letting us settle in, see our friends, have our evenings and weekends free. Pouring us at first gently, and then with more direction and speed, into a frame of mind that compulsively made the work both interesting and fun.

Her task was a daunting one. Every three months she was faced with a new conglomeration of unworldly girls, with a mere sheen of womanhood about them and little else apart from their School Certificates, and in ten brief weeks turn them into embryo Nightingales. Such a prospect would have overwhelmed many a lesser character. But she understood the minds of young women as well, or better, than any other sister I was to know, and those who appointed her must have realised this.

We called her Sister P.T.S. (for Preliminary Training School) as all the sisters were called after whatever they were in charge. She did much of the teaching herself and made even the lectures on nursing hilariously funny, to say nothing of those on anatomy and physiology. The first day we had got going on the skeleton she had my pencil wiggling away on the opposite page, sometimes jotting notes in poetry which began a long trail of poetry writing during my nursing years. This was in no way detrimental to what I was

17

taught. In fact it helped it—by turning some of what she taught me into poetry made me remember it better than I would have done otherwise.

I also wrote long letters to my mother in my spare time. My parents were living in Scotland at the time. My father, who was in the navy, was stationed there and these letters gave my parents a full commentary on what was going on. Now that we have finished the bones', I said in one of them, 'we are doing blood, a heavenly subject'.

Such enthusiasm must have soothed my mother, if she were having any doubts about it.

Apart from anatomy and physiology, another subject that held a mass of revelatory truths, was hygiene. As an eighteen year old who had been brought up in an immaculately clean house, the question of hygiene—other than the necessity to wash my hands at certain times of day and tidy my hair before meals to keep it out of the gravy—had never been an infringement into single thought. But of all the subjects on which we were lectured in those preliminary training days, the importance of hygiene was the one that struck the deepest chord. What we were taught about germs filled me with foreboding. A picture was painted of air turgid with them. Skin infested with microbes from end to end, multiplying massively in the moister parts of the body. Surfaces of a room being harbingers of millions of these invisible enemies. So, to prevent them from perpetrating their evil ways, we were taught what to do about them. This was to establish the basis of all the cleaning, wiping, polishing, disinfecting and sterilizing that was to take up so much of our time. It was a truth punctured into our minds as though they were branded. It formed the rudiments of an awareness that became an eighth skin and it conditioned us to a reasoning that could not exclude this awareness. It awakened a sense that had been non existent but was now as sharp as a razor.

Compared with all this, our lectures on dietetics must have seemed rather like nursery rhymes. Our set was divided into four groups and on two different days these were taken in buses to Guildford for cooking lessons, all part of our dietary experience, and these I can remember quite clearly. We were given demonstrations and then had to copy them in a set time for which we received marks. This had quite all intimidating effect on me and I can recall, with shaming memories, the time we got down to making scrambled eggs.

'Do not wait,' the demonstrator said, waving her wooden spoon in the air, 'till all the egg congeals in the pan on the stove as the heat continues to cook it after it is taken off.'

Not long enough, I found out, as I poured a yellow lake of egg, with a few golden islands, onto the plate. My letters home gave clear indications about my feelings on the matter, 'the very thought of being marked makes me do everything wrong and I always feel sick after eating what I have cooked.'

It was not just with cooking that I fouled up many an early attempt, I found bandaging heads a feat of magician standards. During our bandaging classes we were taught how to make a large abdominal bandage that was much used on the wards and probably still is. During those weeks we were also given medicals, were X-rayed, had B.C.G.s and were in every way possible primed for the next stage of our training.

The beginnings of this came after we had been at the Manor House for about six weeks. We were taken up for the first of three trips to work on the wards for two hours in the morning. The ward chosen for me, and the one in which I was to start my training, was a women's surgical ward called Elizabeth. I took an instant liking to it—the whole place was balmed in sunshine and almost no one seemed to be in bed. My trepidations were also eased by a smiling nurse who came to show round the other probationer who was, like me, going to work there and myself.

However, I did not altogether escape the kind of episode that I had envisaged. One of the patients, probably spying my crisp newness and buckled attention, seized one of my arms as I went by and asked me when she could have her stitches out. With that she lifted up her nightgown, showing me a large part of her bare torso with a strip of plaster cascading down its centre. I looked at her with eyes that felt as though they were bloodshot with embarrassment:

'I'll get a nurse,' I whispered.

'You could have fooled me,' she cackled after me, 'thought you were a blooming nurse.'

Not yet—not yet.

It was the third visit to that ward that really stands out in my memory. Because, after careful and gentle initiations, like watching admissions from a safe distance or helping with lunches, it was obviously considered that we should be shown the real stuffing of nursing as against its silken case. On that day we were shown two conditions. One of whose existence I had been entirely unaware and the other having a name that lurked in history books and Dickensian novels as a fairly common, but nonetheless dread complaint. With the former, a particularly unsightly colostomy, I was totally unprepared but managed to numb my face into the dead lines of custom and habit. Worse, however, was to come with the second case. We were taken behind screens to see an old lady of about eighty who had a cradle over her legs and was shortly to have an amputation for which Sister Elizabeth was preparing her. I had heard her mention the word gangrene but was not prepared for what met my eyes and my nostrils.

On the return journey to Godalming I gave due thought to what I had so unthinkingly taken on. Whatever had been my motives for thinking I would like to nurse sick people, I had not been ready for the raw, the hideous, the stinking, nor had my imagination tried to examine the side of it that was not obvious and simple. I did not know then that I would never again be faced with the kind of shock that both those cases had reverberated through my being. Nor had I any understanding at that time of the compassion that would come so quickly for the sick when actually nursing them. So that whatever was wrong with them, whatever had to be done for them, however much it might outrage my senses in one way, was always to be a smaller part of my total feelings than the ones I had for them. If I could have foreseen this, I might have been less crippled with horror on that third visit to Elizabeth than I was. But for a young girl who all her life had only wanted to dance and whose dreams were mostly wrapped up in art, this seemed like no alternative at all. Thus I sat brooding in the bus all the way back to the Manor House—the other girls chattered away like babbling brooks. But I felt that my whole body had been impaled in stone.

Had we not been kept so busy in the following days, I believe I might have made a conscious decision to quit, but there was simply no time to think about it. Test upon test flew off our pens every Tuesday and towards the end there were four exams and two vivas. The work load was prodigious in those last weeks and I wrote my second complaining letter to my mother, saying that there seemed to be limit to the amount of anatomy I could get into my head.

It was not all work, however. Towards the end Sister P.T.S. gave a party and we entertained her guests by singing carols. Also a dance was given at Charterhouse nearby for which lots were drawn as only twenty five of us were invited. I was one of the lucky ones and got off with an American boy who, with nineteen others, had come over for a year to go to English schools. He was a compulsive talker and regaled me with his plans. He wanted to 'do' Europe and particularly Italy

'I wanna go to Venice—it sounds swell.' He asked me why I had become a nurse and I told him that I really didn't know. He didn't know either. He thought I should have been an artist's model. I was secretly flattered by this double-edged compliment and by his boldness after such a short acquaintance. What Englishman would have dared, or bothered, to say such a thing? But I did not know on what he based his assumptions. My long organza dress that my mother had so painstakingly made a few years back to save clothing coupons was by no means see-through with its taffeta petticoat. I did not extend the subject and anyway he had plenty more to say. He knew a great deal about Italian Renaissance art (a matter very close to my heart as I had recently been to Italy) but, 'unfortunately,' I said in my letter recounting the incident, 'very little about dancing.'

I never saw the loquacious American again but the dance brought me back to life with a vengeance. At the time I was obsessed with going to dances but ten weeks of hard study and discipline, after a few months of freedom, had almost made me forget how much. What was good to find out was that the girl in me popped up through the nurse in a trice.

The term ended soon afterwards. We were due to start at St Thomas on December 12th.

3

The second part of our probationary period we lived at Chelsea Court on the Embankment in Chelsea. Chelsea Court, now with its years as a nursing home long since over, was a delightful place to be. It had the atmosphere of a friendly block of flats, which once it had been, and was run on similar lines and the only complaint I had was that the windows, with their river vistas, were garbed in heavy netting. Everything else about it, its position, its comfort, its proximity to London's social hub, could not have been bettered.

It was equally fortunate that I had been selected to share a room with a Nightingale called Peggy. We had made friends at the Manor House and put in an application to share, so it was not by remote affinity engineering that we found ourselves together, but it was as happy an arrangement as I could have hoped for. The power houses at St Thomas's were very conscious of the importance of allowing friendship free range to blossom in the various nurse's homes, and did their best to assist it. The result, anyway, was to knit one of the best relationships of my life.

Peggy was a girl of infinite variety. Very pretty with a dewy, rosy skin; a neat nose and mouth; hair a buff-honey colour with a small slab of a curl at the corner of her forehead and a range of tufty curls round the side and back of her head, her main feature were her beautiful, large eyes which, if there were a colour between aquamarine (the sea not the stone) and dove grey, that was what they would have been. Those eyes were continually flickering amusement or were open wide in amazement, her eyebrows shooting into her forehead in delectable arches as she spoke with a faint hint of a lisp and broke into frequent pebbles of laughter. During that first year we spent so much of our time laughing. Some hospital anecdote would set us off and we would sometimes roll on our beds in mirth. I cannot remember any other relationship in my life where laughter played such an important part in keeping a sense of proportion or of balancing situations which might otherwise have collapsed. When I think of Peggy now I can always see her sitting on the edge of her bed, taking off her cap, and coming out with a remark that immediately had me crumpled with giggles. But she was much more to me than that. She had a tireless ability to listen and combined an exuberant personality with a total lack of selfishness. Also I have known few people who could discuss others amusingly but without a hint of malice. But Peggy managed this because she did not need to attack others or defend herself in that way. She was a very rare person because she had completely come to terms with herself at such an early age. With her I could hardly have had a better starting point.

It was given an early test. Every morning we were woken up at 5.45am by a paroxysmal bell that blasted its way round the corridors of the home in what seemed like a five minute alarm. At that hour of the morning it probably needed to. Neither Peggy nor I were early birds so this intrusion into our consciousness came in the middle of our night. However, after the first morning or two, as the bus did not leave till 6.30am, we became experts at last minute dressing techniques and were often amongst the many Nightingales flying down the stairs at 6.29, our caps in our mouths, fastening studs and pins in the hall. Sometimes, when we had overslept, there were frenzied torments of dressing in those dwindling seconds because if we were not in time for the bus, it went. This meant thumbing lifts from lorry drivers who were the only drivers on the roads at that hour. The lorry drivers hissed their Westinghouse brakes and Peggy and I and a host of other overslept Nightingales would clamber up into the cabs beside them, all crisp and new in our freshly starched aprons.

We loved those trips with the lorry drivers, spinning through the winter mornings along the hard edge of the Thames, still in the charcoal greyness of the night, with the lamplight shimmering on wet and glossy tarmac, or Jack Frost clothing the branches of the naked trees. It was warm and intimate up in the cab and we felt like fugitives with our cloaks wrapped around us as the lorries bumped along past Chelsea Bridge with the mauve silhouette of Battersea Power Station behind. On past the nest of waterside restaurants and Vauxhall Bridge where, on the left, prefabricated war buildings still outwitted the meagre life the war ministry had allowed them. On past The Tate and over Lambeth Bridge. Out of their way they went, to drop us at the door. How kind they were to us and how we revelled in their company and they in ours. Never once did they see our waving arms and not respond to them. I counted their Good Samaritanism as the first moral plus of our nursing lives.

When we arrived at St Thomas's we went straight to the dining room for breakfast. Our breakfast—in fact our food in general— was little different from other institutional food of that time. For breakfast there would he cornflakes or porridge resembling, with its lumps, a foggy sea of steaming icebergs—but it was hot. We then had a choice, on different days, of a various assortment of eggs. Boiled eggs whose contents clung perilously to the remnants of their paper thin shells. Curdled mounds of scrambled eggs that paddled in shallow pools of murky water. Poached eggs, with their bulbous bodies and aquatic skirts, that huddled together like some strange sea emissions. And fried eggs that often looked like fried eggs but did not always taste like them. The latter were accompanied by tails of bacon. After all this there was bread with a yellow blend of doubtful origin for spreading on it (wartime margarine was still around) and shredded marmalade of which I grew quite fond. We could drink tea or coffee and it was considered real coffee as against the Camp stuff available on the wards.

To be honest, although the food was often odd to look at, I did not find it unpleasant to eat. This wasn't just because I might have had a bone palate or because I was always ravenously hungry. Nor was it because I had not known good food because I had. One of my grandfathers had had a superb cook into whose good books I had wormed my way at a very early age and had spent many hours hanging round the kitchen for treats. My mother also had a flair for cooking and had made the most of her kitchen garden and well thumbed culinary bibles during the difficult days of the war. I had also been lucky enough to spend a year at a finishing school in Switzerland where food was highly rated and there was no such thing as rationing.

However I had known eight years of normal school cooking and this had made me almost immune to what shortages and mass catering can do to food, as well as the fact that I had been brought up to eat everything and eat it I did. At school there had only been one item I had rejected and that was a pale, haemorrhaged beetroot in a glue-like sauce that had so deranged my gastric juices that I would stuff it into Ovaltine tins under the table and later, when the coast was clear, throw it into a nearby lake. At St Thomas's there was nothing like that. No beetroot except heavily disguised in vinegar, and the other root vegetables I liked. There were also good stews, shepherd pies and braised meats. Admittedly the liver, often grey from over-cooking, took some swallowing, as did the cabbage with its jumbo stalks and laboratory smells, and I bypassed completely the khaki sprouts. But the rest was fine. Other Nightingales may not have thought so, but I was, perhaps, easy to please.

No, it was not so much the food, but the time allowed for meals that seemed a factor. Half an hour is an eternity in a dentist's waiting room but it is not much time when the ward that one works in is at almost the maximum compass distance from the dining room and when there are often errands to run, queues to wait in and other interruptions as well—particularly for the nervous novice. Apprehension is the biggest juggler of time I know. It can multiply it by ten or toss it like a coin.

This it did effectively with my first duty in the morning. We reported on the wards at 7.30am and had the job of dusting down one side of the ward per probationer. The wards had fifteen beds a side, with fifteen tables and lockers and thirteen windowsills. All of which had to be dusted and tidied by 8 a.m. which allowed two minutes per bed, locker and table—and a decimal extra for the windowsill. Of course it was possible and of course it was done. But it was an example of the deadlines with which our days were locked. I can clearly remember the effect it had on me. It built inside me an inner clock which operated with minute precision the speed of all I did. Absurdly, you might think, I hardly needed an inner clock with the great cyclops of Big Ben sitting opposite the hospital, thundering out the time so that even if I did not look at it frequently—which

I did—I could not fail to hear what time of the day we had reached. But for me, Big Ben was the very reason for the inner clock because whilst working at St Thomas's it was not possible to manipulate time with excuses. So, on the dot of 8 a.m., the ward sides were immaculate and we were ready to deliver the breakfasts.

Meals for the patients were simple affairs in those days. No menus, choice or complications (except special diets). So the sister would trundle round the heated food trolley, plopping pats of the amounts required by the patients on the plates. On Sundays there were boiled eggs for breakfast that we cooked ourselves in the ward kitchen and, with excessive care, these sometimes remained within their shells. Breakfast was allowed an hour to proceed. Then everything had to be cleared away for the real business of the day to start at nine.

For the first few weeks, apart from the three 'B's—bedpans backs and beds—our main work was *le ménage*. There was 'high dusting'—a difficult feat of moving small hedgehogs of brushes on a pole along ledges so high they could not be seen. Occasionally flanks of dust would sail into the air like poultry feathers—and I would grit my teeth and think they would have been better left where they were. I did not like high dusting because it gave me vertigo.

'Wet dusting' was almost as bad because pre-smog-laws Lambeth grime was high class stuff and because there were no rubber gloves available for domestic chores. Cleaning the boilers did not attract me either as it was such a frustrating business. No amount of elbow grease seemed to be able to prevent scabs of lime and chalk resettling on the surface of the water when they were refilled. I tried hard to win the battle of the boilers but never did. Many of our duties were linked with the invidious disinfectants; the vile smelling lysol and the sweet pea carbolic, which did not like young skins any more than they liked germs. I think the only chore we did not do during those months was polishing the floors. Those were done by the ward maid or the orderly (of whom there were one a piece a ward) and as a result I have always rather liked polishing floors since.

As probationers, much of our time was spent in the outhouses.

The sluice, that projected like a shoulder out of the left end of the ward, had three external walls and numerous windows and therefore was full to the brim with light and air. This also, in winter, made it very cold. So when it was necessary to scrub the worst of the stains off the draw sheets (before they went to the laundry) under cold running taps standing on a stone floor, the icy drafts made the goose pimples on our arms stand up like geese. If germs cannot live under certain temperatures, I do not imagine that many of them prospered there. Compared with the warmth and comfort of the ward in general, the sluice was like a vault. I still have a letter written to my mother referring to the cold in the sluice, as apparently my frosty hands had dropped my fountain pen into a bedpan so it had never stopped leaking since. The letter was written in pencil.

In the other shoulder of the ward, bathed in what seemed like permanent sunshine, although it was probably permanent steam, was the bathroom whose sauna-like qualities and layers of plastic curtaining made. it as warm as the sluice was cold. Therefore I quite enjoyed cleaning and polishing the baths and taps. And once or twice used it as a studio when it came to photographing patients.

In another outhouse the sister arranged the flowers. In those days and perhaps still (although it does not seem to apply in other hospitals) it was considered that flowers consumed nocturnal oxygen to the detriment on the patients, so they were moved out of the wards at night. We took them out but the sisters put them back in the morning. This gave them yet another contact with the patients. One of the strongest features of the Nightingale creed was the very frequent contact between sisters and patients (meals, flowers, numerous rounds as well as nursing even in its simplest form) and, for me, the flower element—returned refreshed, re-watered, rearranged, smelling sweetly—was the one I found the most charming.

Next to the flower room was the linen room about which there was an almost mystical reputation, like a hospital Secret Garden. In its enclaves it held the huge drums of sterilized dressings as well as the linen. All of which was not only monitored but, one felt, registered so that every item could be accounted for. Inevitably it was always locked and the key was kept pinned to the bosom of whoever was in charge. In those first few months I don't believe I even saw inside the linen room and no intruder was allowed near the place without the sister's sanction.

All in all we continued to fulfil, in those first few months, what had been specified for us in the leaflet we had been given about the Nightingale training. In its pages it stated that the early part of the training followed the lines of a domestic science course specially designed to the practical needs of the student nurse. On our duty sheets this was elaborated in more detail under the heading, 'Ward Management', and includes all that I have mentioned and much that I haven't.

Of those simpler duties mentioned in our syllabus, there was one of such concern to us that we were always discussing it. This was the filling of hot water bottles and water pillows. Now, if you think that any fool could fill these receptacles in the proper manner without any training, then you would be wrong. Even now I follow exactly the method taught us, which mostly concerned ridding the bottles of any trace of air. The water bottle was not so difficult; but the water pillow was a major task.

This was a large slab of rubber about 2ft square which was the hospital's major combatant against bedsores. It had to be filled to about half to two thirds full of water and then have all air excluded. To perform this function it was necessary to sit on a chair and fold the three furthest corners of the bottle inwards like a baby's nappy and squeeze the incumbent air towards the bottle's mouth. This often meant a projectile tongue of water being deposited in one's lap with the air still inside. Even if one managed to shift the air, the water had a nasty habit of coming too. More than once I was left with an uncomfortable puddle of water round my waist. Air out, the stopper was hastily screwed before it had a chance to get back in again. The bottle was then tested against one's ear. A mere trickle of sound meant that air was still inside and so the whole procedure had to be started again. Silence meant success. There was still, however, the hurdle of the sister's test. How I used to hope for a porringer to be dropped, or a huge delivery, or a doctor to appear, because the sister's ears were so very finely tuned.

Another matter of dread in those early days was answering the telephone. As a child I had never wanted to do this as children do now. To me a telephone had been a question of alarm, and so it was on the wards. The 'inside' telephone was situated just by the ward door so that the numerous passers by could, by footstep or conversation, inhibit the clarity of what seemed a fairly frequent nightmare of histrionics, and where there was no opportunity to write the message down. The messages from the dispensary were the worst. My uncomprehending ear would pass a poorly heard message to my short term memory and I would blurt out an assortment of words to the sister. And just hope that *duboisine guttae* meant more to her than it did to me.

In many respects, though, I was very lucky because Sister Elizabeth was a woman of much sympathy—not only for the sick. Sometimes she would look down at me—she was a great deal taller than I was—her face a compassionate question mark, as she digested all the doubt that was in my face or on my lips, and gave me a lovely smile. I felt very much one of her protégées and when I heard some of the stories about other sisters I mentally cowered beneath her wing. In my letters home I described her as so charming (heavily underlined). But I think even sisters as tolerant as her deplored ditherers and the bleetings of ignorance and wanted us to show a crisp initiative. That was the impression I got right from the beginning—get a move on, get going.

Most of my first patients on Elizabeth seemed acutely aware of the uncertainties at this stage and made few demands that could not easily be met. But I can remember one or two who were distinctly tiresome. There was a Mrs Cuthbertson, fifteen stone if she was an ounce, and well on the mend, who occupied a bed three from the door. Who, almost nightly as I was going off duty—or any time I was going off duty for that matter—would pipe up in a loud sister-will-hear voice.

'I'll have a bedpan nurse'.

My heart would sink into the grotto of my being at the sound of her voice. How could anyone want as many bedpans as she appeared to want? In those days, there were no curtains that could be drawn round the bed so two screens had to be humped to give her privacy (in the general bedpan round, a screen was merely put at the door and all the women were enthroned together) and then, of course, put away again. The whole roundelay could bring me close to missing my bus. After a time I learnt to creep off duty down the other side of the ward, as the very sight of me was enough to get Mrs Cuthbertson's waterworks going.

Then there was a Mrs Palmer, permed to her scalp, with a slightly whiny voice that I came to connect with the purple grapes that her husband supplied almost daily and which sat on her table. These she liked to have peeled and pipped.

'Because the skins line me stomach and pips go into me appendix.'

Had I been a little more experienced I would probably have given her a curt one-sider about her continual bayings for grape peelings. But I was still at the stage of being a grovelling slave to anyone who asked me anything and this included Mrs Palmer and her miserable grapes.

However, those two women stand out in my memory only because they were the exceptions. The majority was considerate to a fault. I do not remember a patient who did not come in immaculately prepared. Their hair freshly set and often permed as well. Their clothes pristine and much of it new, particularly the night attire. With new flannels and soap, toothbrushes and paste. Most of the patients were working class people, when money was much harder to come by than it is now. Some of them must have spent almost a week's pay on their preparation for their stay in hospital. I used to think that there must be people who could not afford new woollen bed jackets and furry slippers. Where were the real poor? Or was it just that in closeknit communities of which England was made up then, they rallied round in support of prospective hospital interns? Anyway, it was of great benefit to us as one of our first duties on their admission was to see that their personal effects were all. in good order. If it had already been done, obviously we welcomed it.

My letters home were filled with stories of the dying. Three weeks after I had started in Elizabeth I wrote about an old lady who took my hand in hers and asked me the final question. I was nineteen. I had never had any contact with death before except the loss of one of my grandfathers when I was eleven. Now suddenly I was holding the hand of a dear and gentle lady whom I had known for only such a short time and had her ask me if she were dying.

I looked into her soft eyes, the irises ringed in white, her hair as fragile as cobwebs, her breath sinking into her chest, and with a certainty of her impending death, I told her she was not. A glimmer of understanding passed between us. I think she knew I had lied and was glad.

My memories of Elizabeth have laid it to rest as a calm, rather quiet ward. Perhaps this could be accounted for by the fact that it was an eye ward and all those sedate eye patches and straight postures—no sudden movements, had to be so careful—gave some of the ward a glimmer of frigidity. However, my diaries and letters tell me that my memories are wrong. In a letter to my mother I wrote:

'I have not dropped dead yet, but had you seen me last night making twenty beds in twenty minutes you would wonder why not. The ward is full now and hectic all the time—two probationers are off sick and our head staff nurse has come out in a rash all over'.

Was I having doubts about it? Peggy was. She disliked the non stop pressure and the slave like obedience—hands behind the back, feet together, head almost on one's chest when reporting for duty, for instance—and found her sister less congenial than I found mine. We had heard that the standards and discipline were less severe than they had been before the war, but the icons of perfection still wielded their power and gave many of us inferiority complexes or crises of confidence.

Perhaps what saved mine in those days was the off duty times. In those early months I was given the morning off more frequently than the afternoon or evening, so I would catch the bus back to Chelsea Court and change into my glad rags. We were provided with an outdoor uniform but I never wore it except for health visiting. The coat was made of heavy navy wool with Admiralty Arch shoulder pads that knocked an inch off my height, and a three inch wide belt that knocked off another two. The hem was so deep (ah those massive hems of the fifties) that I could have been growing like a giraffe and let it down to fit me still.

I could not have found a garment of clothing that made me look and feel more wretched than it did. As for the hat—a cross between a pork pie and a trilby—it sat sunken and revengeful on my head. I think there was even an elastic to stop the wind depositing it in the Thames or some other suitable graveyard. The more statuesque of my set carried those uniforms off quite well. But the little ones like myself all looked odd in it so I put mine in the cupboard, where it languished with the moths, for four years until I was able to dispose of it for good.

Off duty I forgot all about uniforms, put on the prettiest clothes I could muster, and made for Sloane Street—in those days a place that was quietly discreet and had none of the connections it has now. I would spend part of my allotted time thumbing through books in Truslove and Hanson (then at the lefthand side of the street approaching Knightsbridge) and part at the Kenya Coffee House (now extinct) further down. During those hours I would saturate myself with window shopping, book absorbing, coffee and cakes. I felt free like some wild bird that had been let out of a cage. Never have I forgotten the affection I developed for that street as a result, the shafts of sunlight that speckled adjacent Cadogan Place, and its sheer unturning, undivided length.

My days off, too, recharged me. As my parents lived so far away for the first eighteen months of my training, the majority of my days were spent with friends. If Peggy was free we spent them together and wove them into the maximum of pleasure at the minimum of expense. Otherwise, I would see old friends, godparents and the like, all of whom were very kind to me. According to my letters, my social life was a whirl of dances and invitations to parties. But I can also remember an endemic social shyness and unease under the vivid pictures I painted in superlatives to my mother.

One of these was when I had been asked by the son of a friend of my parents to a dance at Henley. We joined a party of four other young people and the evening proceeded well, along with champagne and reels and laughter. Then one of the party suggested we take a boat on the Thames. The six of us packed in with glasses and bottles of champagne, rowed to the middle of the river and started to drink our way through bottle after bottle. At this stage the other girls had collapsed into the embraces of their partners but my partner and I were left not quite sure what to do next. The arm was there, the breathing in my ear was becoming laboured, a kiss was expected but I had never kissed a man before and I did not really want to start with him. I tossed up in my mind. Had I drunk enough to be able to stand it?

The situation was unexpectedly relieved. The others suddenly got tired of kissing and started to throw all their glasses and bottles into the water instead. Even in this I did not join in as I was expected to. I hung onto my glass because I thought it was pretty and I hated waste (Nightingale economy or wartime shortages?). By this time I was completely out of it. The other girls encouraged their partners to row back to the landing stage and they all flounced off. My poor, rather gauche, beautifully mannered partner stayed awkwardly by my side, and a few more drooping dances did not stop the tears from being very near the surface. Those evenings, with their appearance of shine and elegance hid a mass of heartache.

Nevertheless, my days off, whatever they included, were a perfect foil to the life in Lambeth. There were few temptations in Lambeth for days off and it was a strange place to walk through with its roundabout roads, its sinister little alleys, faceless buildings and sombre lighting. Walking back from Waterloo at night I would often break into a jog trot as though I was expecting a great damp hand to shoot out and squash me on the pavement. But sauntering along the Embankment in Chelsea, with breezes flacking in the trees above or racing under the bridge onto my face, I knew total relaxation.

As my time on Elizabeth came to an end, I expressed regret to Peggy. I did not want to leave the security of what I had come to know about it. I was also worried about my first report. I had heard on the hospital grapevine that Sister Elizabeth was known for her bad reports. As it turned out I was very lucky. 'She is still a little noisy,' it said amongst much else, 'but takes correction well and shows signs of becoming a promising nurse'. What more could I have hoped for.

4

After those three months on Elizabeth (that was an average period in a ward or department), we were required to sign on. Our improved status was acknowledged by the wearing of a black leather belt. This belt had a psychological benefit built into it. Not only had we moved up one step in the nursing hierarchy, but we now had subordinates, because another batch of probationers had been dispatched from the Manor House. With the black belt period I felt I grasped the first straws of self confidence. That confidence was the bedrock of the leap we were to make from our domestic beginnings to considerable responsibility in a relatively short period of time. With the black belt we felt we had the first feathering of Nightingales.

The ward move took me from one end of the hospital to the other. I was moved to City of London which was next to the dining room on the ground floor of the southerly end of the hospital. Not only was its geographical location totally opposite to Elizabeth, so was its atmosphere. It was a men's accident ward and therefore was turbulent, verbose and sparkling. I was to work on that ward twice—in my last as well as my first year. So I managed to see it with two sets of eyes divided by three years of experience.

City (a ward most people seemed to like) immediately evoked the hospital ward of one's imagination brought to life in its entirety. There were always broken legs, mostly of the young, that were on traction, the bottom of the beds heaved up on blocks that were sometimes so tall the beds appeared up-ended. Then there were the knobbly old men with their feathery hair and chomping false teeth struggling to roll their own cigarettes. There were the blue hospital dressing gowns that flowed round the wards, the crackling humour that sped round the beds, the coughing, the spitting, the laughter—it was a lovely place.

There was often a member of the hospital staff on that ward as a patient. The one we had was a blond student in his final year who had a slipped disc. He lay on his side most of the time puffing away at his pipe. From under a curtain of pale, straight lashes, he surveyed the nursing fraternity like a bloodstock breeder assessing yearlings at Tattersalls.

There was also a Welsh houseman who did his own assessing of the nursing bloodstock. Most of the house men were just too busy to bother about junior nurses, but he treated us like women. The student told me in confidence that he had a reputation for being very fast. And, yes, he did once carry my case to Waterloo, but with what gentlemanly poise. He gave an additional buzz to a ward that for numerous reasons had plenty of it anyway: its location just off the downstairs corridor, its bitter sweet sister, its terrace just outside its front windows. It was a ward with a clearly defined spirit. One that seemed to move on its own axis. It cannot be chance that I can remember more about it that any of the other wards I worked on.

I owe to City what I felt were my first experiences of real nursing. Luckily Sister City gave us plenty of opportunities and a longish rope with which to fulfil them. Apart from quickly increasing my experience I came to realise those aspects of nursing that I liked the best.

One of these was its absolute immunity from the normal social warts. Two people meet, one sick in a bed, one healthy beside it and they immediately want to help one another and have every advantage for liking one another as well. Where, I used to think, apart from in wars or calamities, do such instant bonds or felicity exist? So socially handicapped did I feel at parties, for instance, that I could not stop myself meeting people with eyes that were sceptical, critical or defensive. Only when I was involved with strangers in other ways—helping, working, playing games with them—did I relax. It was this other involvement that must have made me like most of the patients automatically. Even those that were difficult, I mostly liked. I have known no other situations where relationships have worked so well with such a wide variety of people. In that way I felt nursing was unique. I became more conscious of this in City than I had been in Elizabeth, partly because of my improved position in the hierarchy, and partly because the men felt no inhibitions about showering a fairly easily turned head with praise.

In some ways it was anomalous that I should have felt so relaxed in City because Sister City was an enigma to me, and one of the most volatile characters in the hospital. She was an undeniably attractive woman with an ebullient temperament and a fluorescent charm emanating from a face that turned upwards like a wren's. Her eyes darted around like little spinning wheels absorbing in microscopic detail all that was going on in the ward around her. Her appearance and her essential charisma were very attractive to the doctors and the patients alike. Yet she was also two women. One witty, sparkling and likable. The other snapping like a terrier, her temper like a blow torch on the faults of her subordinates.

It was the uncertainty with her that made me so nervous. With other sisters, one was aware of one's follies almost before they had happened. With Sister City one was never quite sure. Sometimes I would be performing what I felt to be entirely routine duties, like clearing up the sluice or making a bed, when she would suddenly appear like a kangaroo from a thicket.

'Whatever you are doing now, Nurse Coventry, stop it.'

I can see her now, plucking at the top of her apron and tossing her head from side to side. Of course there was always a reason for it. Like some more urgent work that needed doing instantly—at that second. But I never quite became used to the darting switches of mood and the bloodhound tracker instinct so that there was not a corner of the ward in which one felt entirely safe. My feelings for her were always dodging around so that I could not catch up with them. On her calm days I was one of her greatest admirers. On her tetchy days my letters home were filled with vitriol.

As for work, she was a glutton for nursing herself. She chatted and joked with the patients as she washed, brushed, smoothed and patted around them. First thing in the morning, and often during the day, she would march down the line of beds, the front bib of her apron pinned three quarters of the way up her ample chest and her slightly healed shoes tap tapping on the floor, as though she were inspecting a parade but with intimacy. She was also a brilliant delegator. She organized her ward like a conductor from a rostrum as she stood at her desk waving her vocal baton.

Her popularity with the doctors was well known. Her sitting room was regarded as a haven of good humour and relaxation. I often heard from behind closed doors the throb of medical voices and the trills of feminine laughter. I think there might have been a time when I felt a little jealous of this exclusion. Not from the room but from the kindness she showed so easily to them.

The patients all had a healthy respect for her. If, for instance, she were doing a demonstration to us, they would not have dared utter about something amiss. One example was when she showed us how to give an enema. It appeared so easy that it might have been happening to a dummy. Two pints of rich, green, frothy soap mixture went sliding with lightning speed down the funnel and tube and vanished. The patient did not make a syllable of protest. A docile expression remained on his face as though he was having a back massage. I do not wish in any way to belittle Sister City's skills, which were considerable, but I think it possible that he had been told to behave and not show his real feelings in front of us young girls, who had a lifetime of giving enemas before us and must not be upset at this stage. (Now that I have had an enema myself, I am convinced that no one could endure this most rotten of treatments without howling their dissent at some stage.) Whatever the reason, I approached the giving of my first enema with misplaced confidence. Here was a treatment that was easy to prepare, required no presterilizing (about the only one that didn't) and was—alas how I had been deceived—quickly over.

The poor man who was my first victim uttered a scream almost the moment I had picked up the jug to start pouring. This so alarmed me that I felt the tiny amount of soap that had advanced towards its destination must have done its stuff. So I brought the procedure to an end and waited for the results that never came. Sister City was not at all amused by this waste of time. Had I not watched her demonstration properly? Had I not seen that it had to be two pints, no less?

The next time my turn came round, I grimly persevered, little by little, till all the soap mixture had made its journey. I tried to shut my ears to the sighs that turned to pleas and eventually a shout. Sister City's will had somehow got the better of my cringing nature towards causing someone so much discomfort. So intimidated was I by those first two experiences of giving enemas, I could not find much to like about giving them afterwards.

As City was an accident ward (no Intensive Care then), crises came and went like tides. Sometimes one would go on duty in the morning and find what appeared to be a ward full of new patients. Emergency admissions had meant that recovering patients had had to be moved up in the night to the other surgical wards—Edward, Clayton and Nuffield—that were stacked immediately above it.

I can remember one occasion we had a Norwegian patient who called the nurses 'scrumptious'. Going on duty one morning and expecting the usual greeting, we had seen on his pillow, to our chagrin, the beady black eyes and thick bushy brows of a costermonger, who had been picked up blotto in the Old Kent Road during the early hours. The Norwegian beauty had been transferred to Nuffield. He later sent down messages that the nurses were nice up there but obviously not the standard of those in City.

Blanket bathing the men was fun but I was unaware of some of the pitfalls at the beginning. How a hairy chest takes its revenge on a bar of soap and how ticklish men seem to be in the most surprising places. Naturally, there was a part of their anatomy that we were not allowed to wash. Unless they were very ill or in emergencies and then the more senior nurses washed them anyway (though I do think some wards had different rules on the matter). When we had finished all but the manly parts, we would discreetly disappear behind the screens, with that neatly worded St Thomas's sentence: 'I will leave you to finish off now.'

Most of the men immediately understood this innuendo and picked up the flannel and got on with it. But on almost every occasion I felt an underlying apprehension that the message would not register and that there would be the necessity for explanation. And this, of course, sometimes happened.

Then there were those cheeky ones that liked our discomfiture as a matter of course.

'What have I got to finish off, nurse? Come on, tell me?'

I can remember that our student was particularly fond of this gibe. I think Sister City was anyway a little suspicious of what went on behind the screens. So, often she made it her job to wash him herself.

If I washed him, I sometimes saw her face over the top of the bedspread that joined the screen ends. Although there was usually a message that came with the face, I am sure she was really just checking to see if a blanket bath was all the student was getting. There were times when it was touch and go.

'You are blushing, Nurse Coventry,' he would say as I was flannelling his foot and when he reached for an object from his table it sometimes felt as though a hand crawled round my waist first. Certainly we all fussed over him, his disc and his laminectomy for weeks. I think Sister City was as vulnerable to his pipe puffing, eyeballing charm as the rest of us. When he went, I recorded the fact in my diary with deep regrets. The ward wasn't the same at all. It had lost its cloak and its dagger.

Whatever was going on, Sister City deplored inactivity, so speed was the essence. She would chivvy us around to keep us in perpetual motion As a result, I found that most of the treatments I learnt in Elizabeth, I did in City in half the time. There were, however, moments when this was simply not possible. Like trying to drag four inch straps of elastoplast off fleshy mountains of abdominal stubble. Or weeding around the men's operation incisions for the stitches which had vanished into folds of flab or bogs of pus.

I regarded myself as a reasonably good stitch remover from a nice, flat female tummy, where stitches stuck up like mosquitoes from the wound. But taking them out of a middle aged mass of fatty tissue where the stapphalococci had been busy was quite another matter. I remember once staring helplessly at the sight that greeted me—just a few tramlines of catgut over the healed incision and hardly a stitch peering out on either side. I removed what I could and then began gingerly exploring the vicinity for the remainder with the forceps.

The patient, a lean-eyed cockney with plenty of gab, held his tongue for a while and then said, "Ere, luv, if you dick much daipper, you'll powke the oiyes out of a few Oissies.'

Luckily he spared me the oaths. Plenty of men didn't though. There was one old boy called Mr Nuggett with a walnut face who was shrunken, skinny and enraged with only a fragment of his brain still operating. He would swear at us all day long from his bed on the righthand side of the ward. I cannot remember what was wrong with him, apart from his temper, but sadly he died on us in the end.

'Come here you bleeder,' he would yell across the ward at a nurse who was tripping by. 'Why don't you come here you bleedin' woman?'

Everything and everyone was a 'bleeder', no matter what rank, what sex—bleeders all. I don't know why we found him so funny but his puerile rages kept us all in good spirits. I can see him now with his hollow cheeks and his prattling complaints, his hands like eagles' claws and only a tuft of woolly hair on the top of his head, screaming his commands at Sister City.

She, like the rest of us, never knew quite how to take him. In his saner moments he could be quite disarming. Flashing a dying eye of romance and displaying a wit that must have kept the pubs in Lambeth in a merry humour in his younger days. He never had any visitors, so must have outlived those who cared for him. Or had caused them so much embarrassment, they kept away. He made doing any service for him difficult or impossible. Even presenting him with a bottle for his normal functions would be greeted with, 'What the bleedin' 'ell do I do with that? Take it bleedin' well away'.

In those days, before plastic had taken over, all the equipment was breakable, perishable or heavy. In the case of the urinals, they were made of what looked like laminated glass. They were so tough it would have taken a metal crusher to break them. If they were dropped on the sluice floor, which they sometimes were—galloping across its surface like steel plated hounds—I am sure the floor came off worst.

Bottle rounds, Mr Nuggett apart, were generally an excuse for a few laughs. Whipping out a bottle that had been hijacked from a previous round or hanging on like grim death till the next one and then asking for two. One young man, on a bet, managed to pass forty ounces all at one go. I could hardly believe the measuring can. All the men I had known up to that time had been remarkably weak in that sphere, stopping the car in the countryside to hunt for piddling spinneys, or at garages for loos—and all the petrol that had to be bought as a result. Once I had had the embarrassment of being escorted to the theatre by a man whose addiction to beer and inability to retain it meant that he had to trek twice over the legs of the audience before the interval. I had always put this male weakness down to all the glands that men have in that part of their bodies. Just a fact of life. But City was to change my opinions on numerous matters.

In spite of all the jokes and fun, City was a ward with a tragic heart. There was one very handsome man in his forties who was dying of a particularly virulent and loathsome form of cancer. Its signs exposed him, along with his exceptional size and good looks, as one to whom eyes were naturally drawn. He was the only man who did not appear to blend into City's rich convivial atmosphere. He stuck out fiercely like some great poster.

He was a nice man, a kind man, and the impression I got was that he could bear less being a visible spectacle of a range of distressing symptoms—he coughed incessantly, he spat up blood, he moved round his bed continually trying to get comfortable—than he could facing the bleak uncertainty of his future. His eyes seem to burn like black torches in his face. Never for a moment did those eyes rest. Nor did they appear to look. They just roved helplessly round his face.

His young and rather hysterical wife could not hide her agitation either. The two of them appeared like lost souls whom nothing could comfort. In the end, he died quite suddenly (in my absence). The gap he left was a positive chasm. Some ingredients of some personalities became ingrained in the beds they had left behind.

The worst admission during those months was that of a stevedore who had had a sack of grain dropped accidentally from the deck of a merchant vessel onto his back, as he bent on the quay. We were all stricken by the extent of his injuries which included the rupture of some of his internal organs. His face, mostly unconscious or trying to grasp the last threads of life, was more deeply sunk in pain than any I was to see again. In spite of the morphia he had been given, it had not managed to take that expression away. Sister City was as distressed as all of us. She moved the younger nurses away fairly sharply, as though she felt we were too new and tender to witness such a case. The efforts to save his life caused the ward to stir into vivid activity. It became like an amphitheatre around its intensely concentrating cast. Then the stevedore died and it was as though the queen had been plucked from a swarm. For it fell apart. There was nothing left but three screens, a corpse and its attendants. The rest of us went about distributing the washing bowls and doing the routine, as though nothing had happened at all.

Some tragedies had happy endings. There was a young artist called Richard. Richard was a talented painter with what I felt might be a typical painter's appearance. Soft, rather ragged hair, fawnlike eyes that never hardened and an aesthetic face that mirrored a whole world of innerness. His character was as soft as his appearance and he combined a superficial vagueness with a lucid perception that quickly absorbed the nature of other people's characters, right down into their depths. He was admitted to City after having been severely burned in his studio. He had stepped back to survey some of his work and had tripped over his electric fire and his overalls had caught alight.

When he arrived in hospital he was an appalling sight. The flames had ripped the skin from most of the visible parts of his body, and had bitten deep into the muscles and ligaments of some of it. Pieces of skin hung about his body like flimsy rags or were glued together on molten flesh.

I looked down at the remnants of his body. From a point near his knee, a piece of bone stared hollow and wall-eyed from its vermilion casket. The trouser leg of the other one had welded by the heat into the skin to become part of it. The top of his legs, most of his back and shoulders and face, and part of his abdomen had been spared. The rest oozed and wept with body fluids as the staff worked tirelessly to free him from the remains of his garments. At that stage no one thought he would live.

But Richard never intended to die. He had a fibrous willpower and a tenacious spirit, and he was going to recover. He never doubted it. Nor did he pre-empt the possibilities of a limiting future, in spite of the damage that had been done to some of the muscles of his hands. At every stage he complied, cooperated and never complained through disappointment and much pain. He was the ideal patient.

Much of his body was bandaged for a long time in *tulle gras* dressings. When it was necessary for these to be removed, the various suppurations had hardened them to such an extent that he had to lie in a bath for about half an hour to soften them. Quite forgetting that he was in the bath (there were normally bathmen to cope with the men), I walked in on him. I was quite overcome with confusion, never having seen a man in a bath before. I hastily turned back to the door and was preparing to leave. In his usual relaxed manner, he stopped me.

'Don't be shy. Come and see how well my burns are healing.'

So I stopped being shy and I went to have a look. The results were remarkable. New silky skin covered many of the areas where once there had been raw marshes of flesh. After he was discharged he asked me to a party in his studio (it must have been long after I left the ward, as he had to have so many skin grafts), so I was able to see the place where it had all started. He was a very special person and patient, and remains one of the most powerful images left by City.

Our busiest times were the evenings when eight Nightingales were supposed to be on duty. If we were short of nurses—and the winter months thinned them out—and there was a drama in our midst, Sister's temper would crack a little. She liked the ward to be in perfect readiness by 7.29 p.m. There was no afternoon visiting, except at weekends, so the evening session was a major event. A screen was placed across the doorway until the dot of 7.30 when it came down and the visitors flowed in for half an hour. Then a bell was rung by sister at the desk and they all flowed back again. It was an absolute ritual, timed to the second, and made visiting times much more obvious and definite affairs than they are now. I used to watch the patients heads turn to the door as the screen came down and see them sort out the individuals that mattered to them personally. Then when it was over, the pecks on the cheeks and the promises about the morrow. Sister City was most particular that everyone left on time and would clap her hands and, occasionally, stamp her foot if people dallied round the beds. I cannot imagine what she would have thought about the laissez-faire attitudes to visiting times nowadays—when people wander in and out of the wards even when doctors are present. Good gracious, it would never have been allowed. The visitors got away with as little as the nurses on that ward. We all stuck to her rules.

5

There were many advantages in working in City and one of these was its proximity to the dining room, so that meals became real breaks in which to indulge much more than just eating. It was a hive of gossip and an essential meeting place with those other members of our sets.

It was a fact of life in those days that Nightingales were much closer to the girls in their sets then they almost ever were to those with whom they worked. Only at the beginning of my training, and once later on night duty, did I ever work with those nurses with whom I had started my training. Yet they were my friends and we would all gravitate together when we went for our meals. The reasons for this clanishness, I suppose, might partly have been that the sets were divided by a stratum of seniority—only three months, but at the beginning this seemed like an eternity—where it was only seniority that counted.

The pecking order was labelled by the colour of our belts and uniforms and engraved on our instincts by an automatic knowledge of who was more senior or junior—even in the large quantities of girls who were coming in. It immediately underlined that a more junior nurse—even one who was exceptionally intelligent or skilled—never shared exact equality with one who was more senior in time.

For this reason, as well as our original isolation at the Manor House, our closest friends were nearly always those in the layer of the hospital in which we, ourselves, had first flourished. We all had this feeling about our sets and sets were all different. They had their own sayings, jokes, touchstones and means of communication. And, often, quite different ideas about the hospital.

Only on one occasion did I make a close friend of a nurse who was outside my set. She and I worked together in the cosy intimacy of night duty where the same rules did not quite apply. Apart from her, the numerous shared experiences with all the other nurses with whom I worked, never really crossed the pecking chasm into lasting friendship. It sometimes seemed as though we were almost tribal in our affections and loyalties.

Probably because of this, much of the time when I write 'we', I am only referring to my special contemporaries. Since a great deal of how I saw the hospital came through their eyes and experiences, as much as my own. One of the chances we had to consolidate these was during our meals. It was there, more than anywhere else, that the grapevine soaked up and spilled out its information. The labyrinth of different observations came together into the melting pot of exchanged information and ideas.

The tables in the dining room were large and could hold many more nurses than those with whom we personally wanted to converse. So we got together in our groups round the ends of the tables to divest ourselves of the daily happenings and matters of intrigue. One of the many topics of conversation was the strange view the patients had of us. An early discovery was that nurses are another race. One of us had an experience that perfectly illustrated this.

A patient one day told her in great confidence, 'The upper classes are very nice nurse,. If you ever get to meet any, they are very nice if you do.'

What could she reply to that? She was upper class herself and, before she became a nurse, had mostly fraternized with them. Although there was no particular reason why a patient should identify a junior probationer, mostly seen in a whirlwind of bedpans, as the daughter of some ancient titled aristocrat, the attitude was interesting.

If the patients did not recognize this element in the St Thomas's makeup, it was, I think, recognized by people who were close to the hospital in other ways. It was considered the most socially desirable hospital for young girls about to begin their training, as well as having the reputation for being one of the most highly regarded. So St Thomas's had its double position in the training hospitals' crust. Nevertheless, its trainees were very mixed and included many foreign girls, who supposedly were a mixture of girls with the right qualifications who wanted such an exemplary training. The upper class girls might have been particularly well suited to it, coming from families with autocratic parents or tyrannical nannies.

One of the blue-blooded girls in our midst was a princess, who was a niece of Prince Philip's. She was blonde and pretty in a teutonic way and had a breezy personality and high floating confidence. I never worked with her and, as she was in the set above mine, I was not in a position to pick up crumbs of royal gossip. But I heard that the delectably handsome Prince Philip rang her up frequently. This caused quite a tremor in the nurses' homes.

At that time, I had the chance of seeing him in the flesh myself. This was when I was presented to the Queen at Buckingham Palace in one of those annual Presentation Parties for debutantes long since ended. I had not wanted to take part in the much vaunted season but had spent a year in Switzerland instead. However, I still liked the idea of being presented. My mother had shown me photographs of herself in her white presentation attire adorned with fronds of ostrich feathers—essential in her twenties' year. Following in her footsteps, albeit in a much less ceremonious way, seemed to me automatic.

By this time I was old for the affair—nineteen instead of the more usual seventeen. Sister City, however, was only too happy to give me the day off. So, decked out in a blue-lilac silk and lace dress, with a matching bandeau and veil on my head. I arrived with my mother at Buckingham Palace where we were separated. I was shown into an immense room, its ceiling an elaboration of beauty where, on long rows of giltwood chairs, sat an array of colourful girls. I chatted to the girl next to me in her spotted cinnamon silk, febrile with nerves, as I waited to be called forth.

When this happened I was taken into a room that was filled like a golden bowl with light. On my right sat the rows of parents. On my left, on a slightly raised floor and on two thrones, sat the Queen and Prince Philip. My curtsey to the Queen went without a hitch but, as I dropped on one knee in front of Prince Philip, my left shoe swung to starboard. For an icy moment, I felt as though I was going to be pitched at his feet. I somehow managed to rise fairly steadily and looked at him as I did so. He gave me a twinkle. Then it was all over. I think we were given a cup of tea but I could not swear to it. We rejoined our parents, signed the visitor's book and left.

The next day I regaled my friends in the dining room with all that had happened. But on the ward my lips were sealed. I remember walking round the ward so radiant with happiness, the patients must have been suspicious. In those days I had two selves and they only became one during meals.

One Nightingale in my set, with whom I often used to sit, who had a rather sardonic humour attached to a sometimes lugubrious expression, said she didn't mind being two people. But she did mind the way she was treated. There was her ward sister who did not seem to think that her brain was the sum of its parts; the doctors who walked straight through her and out the other side ; the patients to whom she was a sort of all purpose blotting paper. And even the Pinkie (our name for the ward orderlies who wore pink overalls) had gritty cockney invective that was outside her Home Counties' capabilities of verbal combat. On our lowly rung of the hospital ladder, she felt like some rough earth, dug over from time to time. It summed up a situation we all understood but I did not have quite the same feelings about it. Sister City certainly did not give me the impression she had much of an opinion of my brain— rather the reverse. But I soaked up the problems of the patients and positively envied the position of our distinguished looking almoner. As for the doctors, I had expected them to be supercilious and knew that remoteness was their stock-in-trade. I could never have been a doctor because I wear my heart in the open, but they are the most reserved species—except amongst themselves. Every plateau they reach, detaches them another rung from the common herd.

However, there were points I agreed about. One was the way medical staff can remove inhibitions from the most sensitive of souls. As I had discovered on my first day in Elizabeth, there were occasions when, but for the uniform, one would have felt embarrassed. And so indeed would the patients.

There was one unforgettable incident when I was accompanying a patient called Mr Williams—a rather randy man, a policeman I believe, salute to the force—down to X-ray. We were proceeding down the corridor, when one of the senior staff nurses, a very pretty girl, floated by in elegant off duty clothes that had no part of her nursing self. She looked stunning. Mr Williams did not recognize her so gave her the glad eye crumpled with lechery, as his head followed her moving gait.

Suddenly, through half closed lids, recognition dawned and an expression of shock and anxiety took its place. The metamorphosis and what it unveiled in his mind of past treatments and indiscretions on his part was written on his face in capital letters. It was as though both women had now escaped him: she could not properly be either of them to him any more.

It did not seem to me it was the Nightingale uniform itself that changed our appearances so completely. It was what it did to us inside. My character changed into my mother's. I was born vague, detached, untidy and forgetful (hardly tailormade Nightingale characteristics). Yet, once I was attired in that uniform, I became consistently energetic and organized and could not have been otherwise. I often wished that my mother could have witnessed the only time in my life when I emulated some of the intense energy and industry that motivated her life but which dropped off me instantly when I left.

I do not think there is another place that could have generated such stamina in me and had I stayed there I would have remained like that. I dressed up, I went on duty, I became their sort of person. No matter that I was born to ruminate more than to do. The uniform, as much as the hospital's influence, seemed to propel an internal motor that it gained a natural volition, in spite of whatever genes fate had dealt one at conception.

This by no means made one immune from flaw and failure. Alas, I wish it had. I think the majority of our conversations were directed towards those aspects of personal failure that were either amusing or mortifying or worse. Heavens knows, there were enough examples of those. Having a highly developed sense of guilt, I found every mistake became a small cross on my conscience and I think we all needed the washhouse of one another's experiences to put our own into perspective.

We were still very young girls—and even if we had been older ones—we were intrigued by gossip. Although my memory has not stored one real piece of information that could remotely be called scandal. It simply wasn't that sort of hospital. There were, however, often matters that caused speculation. One of these was a relationship between two nurses. One butch and the other buxom, who walked around the hospital hand in hand and were also allowed to work together. A privilege that I think was rarely granted or even asked for. The majority of us, having just left the pashes and crushes of our school days behind, to turn our attention full bore on men, found all this unusual. But they seemed oblivious to the interest they caused and were always very friendly with everyone else.

This contrasted with the other relationships that went on in the hospital, conducted under the maximum camouflage. Perhaps I have never been particularly observant in such matters. Or perhaps my grapevine did not provide information on the seedlings of romance, only on those of the fait accompli. Certainly the surface flirtations that are expected in the hospital environment were not apparent at St Thomas's. Generally when relationships were on the hob, as I was to find out later when I fell in love myself, blind eyes were tactfully turned. Again and again when hearing of engagements between doctors and nurses, I would be amazed at how discreet they must have been to have kept it all so quiet. Most of my own friends had attachments outside the hospital. Some of them lasting the whole of their training and coming to fruition at the end of it. If there were a romance budding inside, unless it was in our own set, discretion pulled its blinds. One heard about promiscuity, still a rarity to us then. 'Six men in one month' was the reputation that trailed after one innocent looking Nightingale. But the cards of romance were closer held to the chest.

Our visits to matron's office were a frequent topic of conversation. The main office consisted of a unit of rooms off a quiet, well polished corridor where we fetched our post. Matron had two assistant matrons, who seemed to manage most of the affairs concerning the nurses. However, it was not that they were unkind, but that they were so kind that made me respect them so much. I have never found it easy to combine extreme fairness in the hearing of home truths, with the ability to turn it to my own advantage. Or, when asking for a special request, if absolutely sound reasons were given why it would not be possible, to begin to argue reasons why it might be. The whole of matron's office seemed to be bathed in peace that was very noticeable when stepping out of the roar of the downstairs corridor.

But much of the fun we got out of our dining room conversations came from finding guilty little ways in figures of speech to break down the exhaustive standards expected of us into straightforward or outrageous simplicity. For instance, we had sayings like 'fingers were made before forceps ' which would double us up into contortions of laughter because of the nervous rebellion behind it.

By the time we had really settled into the hospital, after six months or so, we found that all we could never have imagined had overtaken us and held us tight. Making fun of it from time to time was one of the ways to revel in what might otherwise have bordered on resentment.

6

After City I was moved to a women's medical ward called Christian and then was sent for three months to the St Thomas's in the countryside at Hydestyle.

'St Thomas's in the Fields', as they called St Thomas's Hospital, Hydestyle, Nr Godalming, came into being in April 1941 after a prolonged period of bombing of the London hospital. Its advent was to coincide with the very time that the mother hospital had reached its lowest period of morale. It was a hospital of cedarwood huts with three hundred and sixty beds that had been built before the war. With the cooperation of the Ministry of Health and the London County Council, an arrangement was made for St Thomas's to take it over. At the beginning, nurses were housed in four private houses in the area. But by the time I went there in 1952, day nurses were accommodated at the hospital itself.

The hospital at Hydestyle was an inevitable scion of the one at Lambeth. The style of the care of the patients and our training as nurses flowed along without interruption. All the sisters were Nightingales. The equipment was all the same and the atmosphere had the breath of Lambeth about it. And yet it was also quite different. The main reason for this might have been that it was in separate units. Unlike normal hospitals, where all the different parts are linked by corridors and lifts and one feels the hand of the hospital upon you wherever you are, at Hydestyle this was not the case. When coming off duty, one stepped straight out into the fresh air. It was a particularly beautiful late summer and autumn whilst I was there—and this diffused the pressure.

The other reason, of course, was the countryside itself. Everything that it has to offer was powerful in its ability to change atmosphere and even though the nursing did not in any way relax its standards, it was, nevertheless, compounded in an environment softened by all that the country can do in giving and releasing a sense of freedom. In some ways there was less privacy. There had been ominous rumours that the rooms in the nurse's home were like stalls and, for some reason, the walls did not go up to the ceiling. The general feeling of the whole nurse's home was lightweight. But it was happy and well equipped with a ping pong table, wirelesss, piano and television. Memories float back. Tennis with Peggy on the courts behind the wards. A green polo neck pullover I knitted myself. Reading *War and Peace* on the lawn. Watching 'Autumn Crocus' on television and the lovers' kiss missing fire at the crucial moment (how could they stop themselves laughing?). My diary tells me that Peggy and I were sharing a room as usual and gave a party for twenty people in that room. We filled the place with flowers, drank cider and beer and danced to the radiogram until 4 a.m. And yet I can remember nothing about that party at all. Who did we dance with? Truant patients? Nubile doctors? Cadets from Sandhurst? It is all a blank.

While I was at Hydestyle I worked on two wards. One of these was the children's ward, America—so named because it had been adopted by some American friends belonging to the Bundles for Britain Association. I had not really been looking forward to nursing children. From brief experience I had found them tiresome to care for. I had always enjoyed just looking at them. There is so much to see. I love their beauty—the translucent skin, the delicate colouring and the features still hesitant before puberty. I love their escaping expressions, boneless movements and their muddlings of words, grammar, form and meaning into a pure language of their own. I love their philosophy and their spine-like observations and evergreen energies. For years after I left St Thomas's I photographed them professionally and could make the most of all this. But closer involvement meant demands I was ill-equipped to give. On a longer term my temperament never adjusted to their Very High Frequency.

The moment I went into America, though, I discovered what everyone else knows—that children not in the best health and without their mothers are another species. A little boy of four was unwinding a bandage from a weeping, crusty eczema on his arm.

'Does it hurt?' I asked him.

'No, it doesn't hurt at all.'

His arms, his legs, part of his body and face were full of fissures and cracks. He showed me his toy crocodile, its intestines bulging out of its tummy.

''Spect that hurts,' he laughed from the corner of his mouth. In the seven weeks I knew him he did not complain once.

Many of the children had the horrible ENT operations and came back, their faces bloody and plugged with swabs. One little girl screamed bitterly and was very sick but said she was sorry afterwards.

'I hope I didn't fwighten Rockiner,' she said indicating six month old Veronica who had had a hernia operation.

Another child had ulcerative colitis—a wretched, exhausting disease. She sat on a bedpan much of the time and occasionally wept, but made no fuss. Then there was Tommy who was six and had nephritis. His tissues were swollen with water and he hadn't long to live but he could still draw and walk, so he made pictures on his slate for the other children.

Bravest of all was Caroline, who was only eighteen months old and had T.B. She was given four injections of streptomycin a day. In those days the antibiotic capsule hardly existed and giving jabs of streptomycin was one of the commonest parts of our routine. They were horribly painful though and Caroline was so brave. Also, although she was not considered an 'open' case, she was isolated for a time in a cubicle of her own. But this did not seem to make her any more demanding. I can see her now with her huge chocolate eyes, her scarlet cheeks and fluffy curls talking to herself in those rather empty periods she spent on her own.

Just before I went to America, a little girl of three died of cancer. In my first few days I heard two children discussing this. Memories of the conversation are not exact, but it went something like:

'Do you fink she went to heaven?'

'I don't know.'

'She was very lickle to go to heaven.'

'Do you have to be old to go to heaven?'

'You don't have to be old but you have to behave. You see you have to be very good up there. And lickle girls aren't very good.'

'Well, if she doesn't know how to behave, she could always be an angel'. This pulverized them into shrieks of laughter.

Sister America had a reputation for being very strict but I can only remember two things about her. Her profile and her devotion to children. Had she been one of the tougher sisters I would have remembered her completely as I remember those who were.

My time in America ended rather sadly. I was feeding Veronica one day and suddenly began to feel she was vanishing out of sight—the strangest sensation I have ever had. I gave her to another nurse and then staggered back to my room. I was admitted almost unconscious to the hospital myself that night. There I stayed for ten days. The worst attack of 'flu—perhaps the only real attack of 'flu I have had.

From America I was moved to George Makins. George Makins was a men's medical ward. Note the exact logic of my ward moves. I had already worked on a women's surgical and medical, a men's surgical and a children's ward. Now it was the turn of the men's medical. Of them all, George Makins was perhaps the most relaxed I had known. Its atmosphere had much to do with its sister who was so pleasant I actually preferred her to be on duty. A very unusual feeling for a subordinate of nineteen. One of the most obvious signs of rapprochement on that ward was the use of nicknames. The patients called me 'Curly'. Except one toothless old fellow with an undershot jaw and eyes as crinkled as raisins, who called me 'The Daily Mirror Girl' after some voluptuous blond (not nude) from page three of his newspaper—of whom, I was, according to him, the spitting image. I had my heart touched for the first time in that ward.

There was a colonel there who looked uncannily like my adored but dead grandfather. But he did not look at me in quite the same way as my grandfather had. He liked to do *The Times* crossword puzzle so, when I was blanket bathing him, we did it together. The crossword was as close as we got. But it is interesting how close it is possible to get to someone doing a crossword. Through the folds of the flannel and working out anagrams, rather disturbing bonds began to develop. It was through him that I learnt that the forties are not the gestation period of old age but merely the consolidation of youth. Whatever our feelings for one another were, however, they were hidden like some valuable mineral under the thick protection of undug turf and were severed, as most are, the moment he was discharged. I never saw him again.

Most of the time that ward was a carnival of humour. Who was it said that for men the whole of life is a game but for women it is serious business? George Makins epitomized the essence of that saying. But not, alas, for all the patients. There was one nasty, old specimen who had been around the ward for three years. What could have persuaded the hospital to keep anyone for that length of time ? It would be unthinkable now. Anyway Mr Lombard's incarceration had given him an inflated self-veneration and a tongue like a hacksaw. He sprayed invective around him, grumbled incessantly and wanted everyone else to feel guilty. If he had ever had a sense of humour it had gone the way that his body seemed so determined not to go. He never seemed very ill, just full of decaying venom. I remember that I once turned on him and after that a reluctant deference to me ensued. But underneath resentment seethed and he told his neighbour, a perky little Irishman, that he thanked God that I wasn't his wife. The Irishman, who often appeared a little tipsy so I wondered if he had a bottle of 'the Good Irish' stored away in his locker, did not agree with him at all. According to the staff nurse who had overheard the whole conversation, he wouldn't have minded one bit if I had been his.

During the middle of my stay in George Makins, a youngish man—a Mr Jack Rock—was admitted and put in one of the beds at the end of the ward. He was a nervous looking chap with watery, jumplead eyes that darted around like lizards, and thick lips that looked as though they had been sewn onto his face. He would fumble with his sheets in an aimless way and never seemed to be occupied positively. One day, for no apparent reason that I can remember, he filled his bed with, for want of a better word, flux.

Sister George Makins was, I think, a little fed up about this. Mr Rock, with his rumbling appendix, was totally mobile. The lavatory was just by his elbow and bedpans abounded and her nurses had better things to do than spend time cleaning up thirty five year olds. I was appointed to do the job and it was during that lengthy procedure that I came, for the only time in my training, face to face with an erection. The significance of this completely passed me by at the time as I still thought—incredible as it may seem—that the male member stayed the same size for all its purposes. Or at least that size had more to do with genes than stimuli.

I was, however, not so naive as to think that there was no 11th factor that I still had to discover (watching mating cattle and dogs had given me a glimpse of what I believed to be the 11th factor). The following night, as I thought about it, I came to the conclusion that the 11th factor was now revealed to me and the chances were that there was no more to it than that.

I remember being a little disappointed but also rather afraid. Mr Rock was still uneasily in the ward with a gut still functioning much too often and an appendix that was helping it to do so. I uttered a prayer that he would not be incontinent again. Or that, if he were, I would not be called upon to do the ministrations. Both my prayers were answered and a bonus was added. Mr Rock was discharged two days later, his appendix having quiesced and not having taught me any more that I did not know before I met him.

But the patient I remember best from those days was Harry. Harry was twenty five years old and had muscular distrophy. He had been a fine looking man from the photographs he showed me, and an ambitious athlete. Destined to go into the church—once a visionary—his disease had crippled his spirit as well. As a result, he was as bitter as anyone I had known. The prayers that had once been his second nature seemed like imposters now. Even to consider prayer, he told me, was like embracing another sort of failure.

Harry was the most noticeable person in the ward because he was tall and, stripped of his muscles, he sat up straight like a funnel in his bed. He had to have his food served on a plate with a warming area underneath as it took him so long to feed himself. I have never felt so sorry for any patient as I felt for him.

I can see him now, his sad eyes denuded of lashes and grown as old in three years of illness as most do in eight decades of living; his busy mind imprisoned in its mortal shell, as he struggled with the minute ever-dwindling activities his disabilities would allow, and my heart ached for him, for the rottenness of his disease and for his strange kind of bravery. He was going to die, he knew. Yet he was not dishonest enough with himself to invent a mothering heaven that would serve him any better than had done a mothering earth.

He asked me straight out if I could face losing everything so young. I remember the exact moment he said those words. Sunshine flooded the ward and the whole of my being was in a vane of joy and happiness (something that happened very frequently in those golden days at Hydestyle). He could not have asked me a more difficult question at a more inappropriate time. In that mood it was impossible for me to imagine the extent of the frailty and hopelessness that had broken him.

He gave me one of his slow, rare smiles, bridging the awkwardness that had come between us. After that I was always especially attentive to Harry. I reached with him the closest I came to crossing the impermeable membrane that is a nurse's armour against those deeper emotions for her patients, that she cannot afford to feel.

Many of the patients in George Makins had come down from the wards in London and this, I believe, frequently happened in the latter part of their treatment. I remember them being pushed around the paths between the wards and the thick, red blankets tucked around them.

Towards the end of my time at Hydestyle I started to get restless. Without even a bicycle—how I regretted disposing of mine at sixteen, thinking I would never use it again—getting around was difficult and expensive. I have been told since, that the hospital paid for each of us to have a weekly trip to London. But I cannot remember that. Just that I thought the fare very expensive and how, increasingly, I wanted to go back. As we moved into autumn and the dews thickened and the damp was no longer lifted off the earth by the sun, but lingered chest level, Peggy and I began to count the days.

And so, at the end of September, it was back to Lambeth and its tighter rules and regulations, that we started our second year.

7

It was about this time that I felt that I had got the measure of most of the intricate clock-like mechanisms that made this mighty, medical institution tick.

St Thomas's was almost too large to be considered a community as I understand one. It was nevertheless an extremely well knit establishment. In a way it was like a vast beehive with all its occupants, including the patients, performing with an instinct and a reason that had become locked together in their minds. There was a grand feeling of ceremony about the hospital and its endemic regulations that was the result of long years of meticulous organization; an identification with being amongst the best, if not the very best of all. I am sure that there was not a person who worked there in those days who did not feel a phantom finger on the shoulder. Like a chessman being moved soundlessly round a board. There was something large we had to live up to and the compulsion to do so injected its own drugs into our bodies.

The most obvious example was matron's visits to the wards. The fact that these were common did not mean that they could be treated with any less respect than if they were rare. Before her arrival, we swarmed around the ward to create the impression of total harmony and orderliness. Of course, the wards were always tidy at the times of day that she came round, but before her visits they looked like centenary postage stamps. Even the sickest people were somehow made to look much better than they were. And those who were recovering and up, went back to bed and sat neat and combed, with their newspapers folded and their tables across their beds. Along the sides of the wards the lockers rose out of their knick-knack coverings. The flowers swelled in health. The screens and trolleys were lined up like sentrymen in their appropriate habitats and the ventilation and temperature of the ward was so perfectly balanced, it would have warmed the finest bottle of *Chateau Lafitte*.

Curiously enough, I do not remember those visits being accompanied by any real tension. Perhaps this was because the standards and the tension were already there—endemic in the ward system. Or perhaps it was because of the character of matron herself. A woman of reserve, discretion and gentleness, with what one felt was rock-like balance, she was the prime example of a top Nightingale. Having been through the whole hospital mill herself, she must sometimes have observed with humour the attention given to some of its least important activities and the human frailties that touched them. Nevertheless, it was an important part of our training as people, as much as nurses, that they remained as they were.

By some strange coincidence, matron and I frequently passed one another on the staircase. She would be in ascent with neatly trimmed steps. I would be flying down, four at a time like a barnyard fowl. Sometimes I would see her through the ragged cage of the lift shaft and try to stop my airborne legs in mid flight. But I was never in time. As we faced one another, she soothed me with gentle remonstrations. Had she ever gone as far as enquiring about a possible fire, she would not have said it sarcastically, like a porter. But with real concern, as though I might have some vital information that had yet to reach her ears. Running down the stairs or in the corridors was probably the one rule that I broke fairly often. With interminable distances to cover and various deadlines to meet, the two could sometimes only be joined by running.

To the other rules of the hospital, however, I was conscious of being subserviently glued. There was, for instance, the rule of the bedspread. When we made the beds, the counterpane with its central hospital emblem had to be put so that the emblem was facing the bottom of the bed. Whilst making the beds we were usually very careful to perform this ritual accurately. But sometimes it was inadvertently put upside down and then the patient had the benefit of looking at it. However, this was definitely a faux pas and if spotted by the sister or any of us, a quick switch round was necessary.

One day, in a side ward, there was a patient with radical views who happened, also, to work in one of the out-patients' departments. She used to watch us making the beds with interest. When it came to the counterpane, she wanted to know why it had always to be put the same way.

'What would you say if I demanded to have my counterpane the other way round?'

I looked at her with my regulation eyes and tried to match her cunning. 'I would say you were a revolutionary.'

A few weeks later this ridiculous conversation appeared in a medical magazine. Feeling a fool I grabbed the next opportunity to rush down to the department of my, by then, ex-patient to accuse her of putting our idle chat into print. She denied all knowledge of the affair and swore she had said nothing so, unless there had been an invisible third party eavesdropping, we realised as we laughed in mystification, somewhere else in the hospital a similar exchange of opinions must have taken place. It did not seem possible, but must have happened, which just goes to show how deeply involved we nurses were in the hospital's influence.

There were one or two other rules in bedmaking that I think were unique to St Thomas's. Such as the pillowcase openings all having to face away from the door. And the bed castors—which were large and, left sticking out, could easily have broken an ankle—being turned in at the end of bedmaking, to run parallel with the sides of the bed. It all went towards making a more perfect looking ward as well as being practical.

Frequently holdups were the regulations connected with sterilizers. There were times when emergency trolleys were needed, when the sterilizers had just been cleaned and filled but had not yet boiled. Or when instruments had just been put back in the water so that sterilization had to be recommenced. I remember the anxiety and impatience that would cause. Waiting for intractable minutes to pass before all the fishing around for porringers, instruments, needles, tubes and rubber gloves—that floated on the top of the water like blubber—could begin. Then there was the sin of putting some unsterilized object in the water when the sister had some special piece of equipment bubbling away for a doctor, who had just arrived on the ward to deal with it. As the sterilizers were so centrally placed there was no way one could escape the tales they told.

There were, of course, many rules with regard to our relationship with the patients—most of them obvious. But one matter the hospital was strict about was the receiving of presents of gratitude. We were allowed a communal box of chocolates—or similar that could be divided and. consumed, such as a cake. But no other presents and certainly not money. Money, anyway, would have seemed ethically wrong, but had a patient wanted to give me a handkerchief, a bracelet or a rose I would have been delighted and accepted it, had it been allowed. Even in the private wing where patients were obviously better able to afford such things, I do not ever remember them being given. It was just a rule that everyone seemed to know about.

Apart from the numerous rules attached directly to our work, there were other matters of underwritten importance in the hospital regulations. One of these was, quite naturally, our appearance. To start with our hair, that multiple harbinger of bacterial nasties, had to be collar-free with no fringes. In fact, in those days, the matter of hair was less of a problem than it might be now, because most young women had permanent waves. These had the double effect of ridding hair of most of its life as well as immobilizing it. Those of us who had escaped the frizzy torment of the fifties' perm, had chopped arrangements or longer locks scooped into invisibility under our caps. As for our faces; no serious makeup, of course, but we were allowed a dusting of powder.

With regard to our uniforms, we were obliged to make up our caps ourselves. This, in view of its shape and elegance, could be quite a feat, as some of the results of the less skilled Nightingale seamstresses showed all too clearly. It was a matter of threading tough cotton round the edge of the cap to pull it up into a circle, matching its top. But it often resulted in a sort of officer caplike peak or ice cream cone, however hard one laboured to achieve the appropriate pill box shape. As it happens I was never reprimanded by a sister for a cap that was bordering on greyness, but I was lucky, because I found them fiddly to make—and regretted disposing of one to the laundry whose shape I had managed to get perfect. On cold days we wore our cloaks around the hospital or in its immediate environs, but we were not allowed to go into public places with our cloaks on, not even to a shop. To do that we had to wear our Gorringes coats and hats or change completely. It was always the latter I did. Naturally, I would never have broken the rule of going out in my cloak. No one did—it just wasn't done.

The regulations affecting our off duty seemed quite reasonable ones. In the first year, as probationers, we arranged our own off duty on the wards amongst ourselves about a week ahead. Later, the sisters were, on the whole, most cooperative in helping us to achieve any particular time off we wanted within limits. If we had an evening off we were expected to be back in the nurses' homes by 11 p.m. with occasional concessions till 2 a.m. for dances. It wasn't always easy to persuade whoever one was out with that these rules actually applied—and that one got into trouble if one broke them. There was many a hectic scramble from the back of taxis or the front of cars to get the key in the lock in time.

The sisters and their second-in-command, the charge nurses, had alternate weekends off, as a result of which, the most senior staff nurses were often in charge of a ward on a Sunday morning. And therefore in a position to conduct the Church of England service that took place in every ward at 11 a.m. Any other nurse who was good at sight reading would play the piano for the hymns and the rest of the nurses sang. I did a great deal of singing in my probationer days and later. As a staff nurse, I was to conduct many a service. Once, not long after the Queen had come to the throne, a patient chirped up that I sounded as if I were Her Majesty opening Parliament. As the pitch of my voice rose I could hear the similarity myself.

If we had our off duty on Sunday morning as probationers, we were expected to attend the hospital chapel service and there were regular daily prayers on the wards at 8 a.m. and 8 p.m. The sister said them at the desk and all the nurses knelt by the door. Thus a blessing was given for the day and the night. Prayer seemed to play an important part in the hospital system and it created a cutting edge for all the regular routine.

Christmas was celebrated by numerous services. On my first Christmas, while I was still at Chelsea Court, Peggy and I and all the rest of us got up at 5 a.m. to get to the hospital in time for Holy Communion at 6.30 in the chapel. Then, after a party in sister's room, we returned to the chapel for a carol service at 11 a.m. In those days the staff nurses did all the work on Christmas Day. The probationers were allowed to spend the day entertaining the patients and were even allowed to roam the hospital and, in the afternoon, went round singing carols. At tea time, the hospital Santa Claus (Dr X) presented each patient with a present from each ward's own Christmas tree. It was a beautifully organized day and gave a tantalizing glimpse of a hospital system caught unawares. Almost like a great giant who dozed while all its happy slaves danced and sang around it.

One of the relaxations at Christmas, was that we were allowed a little tipple in sister's room sometime during the day. This added to the euphoria of the occasion in a way that could not be easily understood in the changed world now. On my second Christmas, I was on night duty and found a bottle of gin on the side in sister's room. It looked innocuous enough—I had never drunk gin before and never did again—so I poured myself a good half thumbful and sat down for my off duty period with Anya Seton's romantic novel *Catherine*, sipping neat gin.

The first change I noticed was that the print on the page of my book began to change from the Roman alphabet I used to see then, to the Greek one I see without my spectacles now. As a result, I immediately felt very sick and raced to the basin in the flower room. Miraculously, I recovered. The earth that had moved like a quake beneath my feet, steadied. The flowers that had quadrupled in number and become wildly impressionistic came back into focus. All was normal or almost normal again. Never can sobriety have been so swiftly regained. The nurse in charge suspected, but the sister never knew. I do not know if it was my training that so quickly redeemed me—determination and self discipline reorganizing my metabolic functioning. Or whether I had rid myself of most of the gin. It has lasted a lifetime. Even now I cannot smell gin without feeling sick. But I was glad that I had not become an inadvertent cause for changing the hospital custom about Christmas drinking.

Of course, the most stringent rules for the hospital concerned the giving of drugs. Early in our training we were given a leaflet concerning the Dangerous Drugs Act, and the hospital regulations applied to them, given under numerous headings. As student nurses, we were not responsible for ordering any drugs from the dispensary. It was the storing and giving of them that became a minute precision operation.

On the wards there was a drugs cupboard with an outer and inner compartment. All the DDA drugs went into the inner compartment which was locked with one key. Schedule I and 4 drugs and any other drugs at all, including any that the patients might have brought in with them, were kept in the outer compartment that was locked with a second key. Those keys were then pinned to the dress of whoever was in charge and never handed over to anyone else on whatever pretext, until the next person in charge took over. The actual giving of drugs followed all the rigorous patterns that every nurse knows so well. There was such a system of stages to be gone through and, even if a drug was needed in an extreme emergency, we were never allowed to skip a single one of them.

Years later I had reason to find these rules exhaustingly tight. My son—then aged six—had been admitted to hospital for an emergency appendicectomy which was satisfactorily accomplished (this was not at St Thomas's). The next day he suffered from severe colic and his whole abdomen was distended with air. As it was Sunday and no doctor was readily available to write up on his drug sheet some simple medicine that would have relieved him, the nurses contented themselves with giving him the aspirin that was written up for him. The asprin worked only briefly and then the pain swamped him again.

I had never seen a child in more pain than he was—it was not just a mad mother's vision. I found myself begging them to give him the appropriate drug anyway. Instead my son had to wait till the evening when a routine visit from a doctor gave him at last what he should have had hours before. Relief came to him so quickly afterwards that I felt a surge of anger that he had been made to suffer so much for a wretched hospital rule—that, of course, I knew they could not break.

However, at St Thomas's there was a completely different attitude regarding pain. It was the enemy to be fought at every level. We were taught numerous ways to relieve pain and, if they were not effective, a doctor would be found to give patients the best possible drug to make them better. In all the years of my training, I can remember not one patient who was allowed to suffer the sort of pain that my son had suffered that day. So I discharged him and nursed him at home.

That instance was perhaps the first time I had the occasion to judge one of the supreme merits of the Nightingale training. There was no room in its ethical philosophies, from base to crown, for one single item of casualness. That was what all its rules were based upon.

This was what I used to feel as I tore up the stairs with half a minute to spare before I was due on duty. If that training had not taught me that I could never be late—nothing could. But it had taught me and I was never late.

8

At the end of our first year we had a period of lectures followed by exams. If we passed those satisfactorily we became staff nurses and our belts changed from black leather to stiff starched white. In most hospitals a staff nurse is one who is fully trained At St Thomas's it meant that we had moved up an important nursing rung and were no longer probationers. We had entered an interim phase. Many new situations faced us as staff nurses and one of those was night duty.

I was later to look back on my training as having switchback tendencies. The probationary period had moved slowly and surely upwards without a break to one level. Thereafter there were one or two sharp dips, losing some of the ground gained rather quickly, before coming out of it the other side. My periods on night duty were to signify most strongly those switchback feelings. My first three months on night duty included the most gruelling pressure under which I have ever worked. My third spell, nearly two years later was, perhaps, the most satisfying of all my training and quite redeemed the worst of the memories of the work we were expected to do as junior night nurses.

In those days, night duty was divided into three-monthly spells with twelve nights on duty and four off. In each night duty section there were six periods of duty and six of rest, with seventy two nights worked and twenty four free (I believe the current arrangement is about even periods on and off duty). Working twelve nights in a row did seem a longish period. But in truth I did not mind that. It was the quantity of the work expected of us that nearly broke me.

The duty period was straight 9 p.m. to 8 a.m. We arrived at the hospital by the usual coach trip from our various nurses' homes scattered around London (Chelsea Court came to an end with our probationary days over)—about half an hour before duty for our 'breakfast'. This consisted of boiled beef and dumplings, curried eggs, macaroni or whatever, followed by milk pudding or apple custard. In fact, the same as the day nurses had had for their dinner. It is strange now to remember how our half-sleeping bodies could be confronted with the sort of food that might have been more suitable for a lumberjack and not feel revulsion. On the contrary, I quite enjoyed this sort of meal before night duty and did not give the matter a second thought. We also came back for a second dose of the same food in the middle of the night.

During the first meal, it was read out on which wards we were going to work. Because there was a limited amount of staff, and because the pressures on each ward varied from night to night, we were frequently moved around the wards. This, however, mostly applied to the middle section of duty—those known as extras or specials. The 'firsts' and 'seconds'—the latter name applying to the more junior—remained as static as possible for obvious reasons, although the nights off element inevitably caused complications. The whole arrangement was quite different from the day nurse set up and required much adaptability.

I think most of us adjusted quickly to night duty—adjusting was part of our training. However, I did take some time to get used to the hospital clothed in its veils of darkness with its vast expanses of almost empty, echoing corridors, dimly lit, through which one perambulated night after night. On that first night duty when I set off for my midnight meal, hurtling down the stairs in my usual fashion, with my shadows arching their backs on the walls and chasing me around the steps, I would sometimes arrive in the downstairs corridor and find that I was the only living soul in its entire length. I was never frightened of darkness as a child but those swelling thoroughfares, soaring ceilings and the silent void of the night-time at St Thomas's unnerved me at times. Reaching the dear, old dining room with its soothing lights and wafting smells and clumps of chatting night staff was always a relief.

On the other hand, working at night had many compensations. I never got tired of greeting the dawn after a night on duty. I can remember so well watching the black masses of buildings reclothed in the shape and colour of stone; the rising light above the stillness and the numerous crests of migrating birds and I found them pleasures that I could not have appreciated in the same way had I just woken up. It wouldn't have been the same, either, if St Thomas's had been huddled up in the city (no aspersions cast here at dear St Bartholomew's, singing with whose choir has given me some of the happiest days of my life). Or trailed along the skirts of the suburbs but enshrined as it was on such a majestic reach of the Thames, with the glamour of the Houses of Parliament opposite— their windows sometimes burnished by early sheets of sun or stained red from a warning sky—and four visible bridges from the ward balconies, the mornings rose like banners.

My first night duty was on Charity Ward, a women's medical in the second most northerly block. For some reason—perhaps matron's office had suspicions about me—I was never appointed to work on a men's ward at night, except briefly to fill in. Charity was the first of many women's wards to which I was allocated. It was a ward with a kindly sister and I am sure was a happy ward as a result. But for me it was always connected with one of the two really unsatisfactory periods of my training. In other words the turmoil of work we were expected to do in the early hours of the morning.

The main body of the night was often fairly calm. After I had returned to Charity from my midnight meal, I then had an hour off in the sister's room (ward weather permitting). It was during this period that Night Sister did her rounds. That was always a hurdle and everyone was thankful when it was over.

For the middle period of the night my duties were mostly in the outhouses. Whilst the nurse in charge supervised the ward from her desk at its centre, the light above it drawn right down on its adjustable flex so that, incarcerated in its blue wrappings, it very nearly touched the desk; and the extra nurse was assuming special duties or acting as her righthand woman, I spent a large part of that period in the kitchen.

My main activity was to cut the bread for breakfast. In this menial task I remember taking great pride. There was no bread cutter and the bread was never sliced. We had to cut it, knife in hand, in paper thin slices, buttered first. Luckily the consistency of the bread was nearly always perfect. Otherwise, no doubt, I would have found the whole operation extremely irritating but the bread was never crumbly or soggy, it was perfect slicing bread. Once sliced and buttered and stacked, it was wrapped in wet towels to keep it moist and then put on the side for the morning. In those kitchen hours it was also necessary to defrost the fridge once a week and also prepare the tea trolley for the early morning cups of teas. I used to get everything as ready as I could—putting out the cups, dribbling milk into them, tea in the pot, sugar to hand, everything lined up ready for the 'off'.

One kitchen night, I had an exciting break in what must seem an otherwise perilously boring routine. The student whom I had nursed on City and who was still around the hospital, about to take his finals, must have got wind of my nightly solitude. He appeared from nowhere like a phantom in my kitchen and embraced me like a man. Whether he did the rounds of the kitchens, I had no means of knowing but he seemed pleased that he had tracked me down (revenge or reward?). After a while, he had had his fill and vanished and never returned. Very inexperienced at this stage of my life—I had got little further than dance floor gropings during the last dance when the lights went out, and my misfire in the boat at Henley—I had never been approached in a kitchen before but obviously they were easier, cheaper and quicker and, I have to admit, no less fun. As one of the outhouses clustered round the end of the lift shaft, it was an easy target for predators and, if murder had been in his. mind, it could have been quickly accomplished without anyone disturbing him. His visit was, I think, the only stimulating event to happen to me doing those three months (if one does not count my brush with gin). I would have welcomed any amount of amorous visits from him and was a little sad I did not get them.

Of course, on busy nights I did not spend much time in the kitchen myself although, as the most junior person on duty, the work I did was just basic nursing again. When I remembered how confident and established I had felt in those halcyon days in George Makins, my labours in Charity levelled that back to the ground. Sometimes I spent the entire night belting up and down the ward without a break. But even in Charity there were many peaceful nights too until, at least, about four o'clock in the morning.

At about this time I would start to prepare for the pandemonium of the morning to begin. I would stack bedpans in great heaps—with cloths between them. Get ready mugs and bowls and porringers, lists and linen. Before the dreaded hour arrived, I felt like a horse in a parade ring before a race. Eager to get on with it, but restrained, as they were, by the clock.

I was supposed to get going by 5 a.m. but, disgracefully, I nearly always started my work earlier. At 4.45a.m., when Big Ben's smaller hand had moved close enough to five to clear my conscience, I would hustle off to the sluice and heave out the first stack of bedpans and race along the rows of sleeping forms to the bed at the end. Hardly a patient was awake at the terrible hour, and who could blame them? Yet they all became accustomed to bedpans being wedged under their sleeping buttocks, produced what was required without a murmur of complaint—bless them—and fell back to sleep again after the bedpans had been removed, as though nothing had happened. They were so used to this ritual I am sure, after a time, it barely disturbed their consciousness. It was all performed in total darkness, as the ward lights did not go on till six. The whole operation was on tiptoe and in whispers. I cannot remember now how long the bedpan round took. But as Charity was a medical ward as heavy as any I was to work on, it would undoubtedly have been quite a length of time.

When the bedpans were washed and stacked, there were the temperatures to take. Again semi-sleeping mouths would open like little birds for food, as I popped in the thermometers, and pulses were sought amid the bed clothes. Pulses could be taken in a quarter of a minute and multiplied by four. But temperatures had to stew. Time, again, would evaporate.

At six the ward lights went on, which made matters easier. Next item on the agenda was dispensing the washing bowls and tooth mugs. When these were cleared it was time for the tea round. Often the fitter patients would help with this, but if I did it myself I would rush the teapot across the top of the cups as I had watched the practiced hands of cafeteria assistants. At some stage those thirty cups—Charity was always full—were collected and washed, but when I managed to squeeze that additional round into my schedule, quite escapes my galloping memory.

Making beds followed. Generally two of us did these together. Crises could, and did, sometimes make it one. This did not mean standards could slacken. Linen pristine, pillowcase openings away from door, emblems downwards, castors parallel with beds.

After the bed-making, my momentum began to ease a little. There was still the 'bowel' sheet to fill in, hot water bottles to fill, specimens to take, and the outhouses to clear up. If most of this had been done by 7.30, I knew I would make it on time. The feeling of drenching relief that accompanied this realisation and the sheer basking in the witching hour of 8 o'clock reached intact with nothing left undone, had an emotionally distorted uplift that lives with me still. It was like the end of a marathon, in which every fibre and nerve was stretched to its limit. The intense concentration required during those fleeting hours saturated me and made no allowance for side stepping, so I found, for the only time in my training, that I developed a cool, almost ruthless, attitude with the patients—whipping aside conversation or anything that could interrupt the impetus to do what had to be done. Little darts of guilt I felt made no difference at all to my rushing sense of urgency. In the whole of my training I had only one real grievance and one feeling of a burden unfairly placed. It was what we junior night nurses shouldered in those first three months on night duty.

Sheer willpower nearly always got me off duty on time. At the breakfast we eat before going back to the homes to sleep, I would study the vacuous expressions of my contemporaries and notice some of the empty places of those whose scrupulousness had, perhaps, detained them. I don't believe I ever felt much appetite—just a burning sense of release. At that time, Peggy and I were in a nurses' home in St John's Wood. That I could not find it now, let alone describe it—when all the other nurses' homes remain vividly clear and locationally exact—must give some indication of how little conscious energy there was left over to expend even on simple matters of observation. That it was quietly situated was the sum total of legacies it left me. For the first month while I was there I was able to sleep quite easily; the youth-over-exhaustion equation gave me eight straight hours without interruption. But suddenly I began to worry that I would not sleep and therefore be incapable of getting through the work the following night. And this began to happen. The Home Sister was most kind and gave me some bromide to put by my bed: 'knowing it is there will help you to sleep'. But during all the remainder of those weeks I waged a battle with sleepless days. Disinclined to use the bromide and yet, knowing if I didn't, I would face an even greater task as a result.

To have expostulated so much about one small, not very significant part of my training surprises even me, for my experience must have been common to all junior night nurses in major hospitals at the time. So why did it bother me so much and raddle my memory and even my conscience now? Perhaps it is to do with some deep childhood inhibition about time scales, preparation, being ready, getting finished, which our training certainly cemented into place. There was not the attitude at St Thomas's, either, that the day nurses could take over what we had left undone. They had their own work to do and we had ours. We stayed on duty until it was finished.

Shortly before those three months were over, I sprained my ankle during one of my nightly flights down the stairs to my meal—crumbling in a heap at the feet of a houseman. Entirely my fault, of course, but I can still remember the prunes and custard that moved like slugs down my throat, and how sick I felt afterwards. The 'firsts' bandaged up my ankle as light as she dared on my return to the ward, and some saint must have been at my elbow that night, for it was an exceptionally busy one, yet, somehow, I reached the end of it intact. On that occasion, I was going on nights off and knew that when I returned I had only one more period of night duty. The end was at last in sight and, although my ankle would have been better with a longer rest, I returned to complete my stint with every night fulfilled—one that could be crossed off never to return.

Later on, I was to have three more stretches of night duty, but it was to the second of these that I now look back with such affection. It restored both confidence and pleasure in a style of nursing that had ample opportunity to offer both. That third period, nearly two years after the first, was spent in Alexandra, the women's accident ward. Which must have been one of the very first to have been destroyed when the rebuilding programme began.

Alexandra was on the first floor of the remaining most northerly block, directly under Elizabeth and another ward called Beatrice, which was on the third floor at the top. This block had had a mighty shaking during the war and, although I never went into Beatrice, rumour had it that there were cracks in the ceiling so there was a certain anxiety that the plaster might take it into its head to shift. As far as I know, however, the bulldozers got there first and took with it the two other wards with which I had had such spiritual propinquity. There was nothing about Alexandra to look at that was special or different from the others (except the oak strip floor seemed a deeper colour). But to me it had an atmosphere that was unique unto itself, inspired and characterized by a gem of a sister with whom I felt I had a special bond.

By the time I worked in Alexandra I was senior enough to be the 'firsts' and therefore was in charge of the ward and liked the responsibility. I grew to feel that night duty held in its grasp the crux of a patient's recovery, so always went happily back after a period of off duty. When that night period came to an end, I relinquished my post with a sense of affection and regret. My mental ease was reflected by the fact that in the day I slept as one drugged by hemlock and found ample time and energy for socialising in between. A point-to-point one afternoon, my diary informs me, a lunch in Chelsea the next. My sleep quotient for those two days was minimal and yet it did not seem to affect my work at all. Contentment seems to provide at least half one's energy—although if Night Sister were to read these words I would still be anxious that I might get a dressing down.

Alexandra was a ward that probably made me more mentally alert than I have ever been. And there was a good reason for that. There was a patient who was recovering from an operation and was staying in for a further period of tests. By the time she had been in the ward for three weeks, I had come to know her well from the conversations we had, and found her a most charming and sensible woman. However, there were times when she appeared to sleep fitfully and, from observations, I wondered if she might be a potential sleep walker. One night I heard her making uncharacteristic noises, so went over to investigate. She stared at me from huge, vacant pupils and then seized the top nut of an oxygen cylinder that had been used for the patient in the next bed, and caught my neck in the vice of her flexing elbow. There was a great deal of strength in that thin arm, I found as I struggled to free myself. Fortunately there was another nurse nearby, who pressed the emergency bell.

Within a few seconds—I'm sure it was only a few seconds—a houseman appeared by my side to extricate me. The woman was heavily sedated—paraldehyde was used, I can smell it now. By the next night, she appeared to be quite herself again. What had happened to her that night remained a mystery and I don't think a rational explanation was ever found. Certainly she did not appear to have any personal grievance against me. From that time on, we were the best of friends again. I think she was quite unaware of what had happened. Who knows that she might not have been caught in a time warp of terror that can encapsulate a waking moment in the dark when location, self awareness and even life have shrivelled to nothing, and one feels a sense of groping for reality, punctured by a fear so profound it knows no depth. (I have had this happen to me once or twice when I was perfectly well. Had I been ill, it might have extended to alarming behaviour.) The whole episode seemed quite unreal afterwards. I have a personal horror of suffocation—strangulation, choking, drowning, to me would be the worst ways to die. Yet, when one is involved in a crisis like that, however acute, one is too busy to be aware of the implications, as one would be in moments of rational thought. Or even of the pain. Afterwards all that comes. But, if you are a nurse in charge of a ward, there seems to be an emergency system in your body that immediately operates to protect you. Shock was somehow absent. My neck ached. I felt very tired for a short time. But that was all.

There were a few other patients from Alexandra who have left their memories. A Mrs Robertson had had a small stroke following an operation. She was in her seventies but should have made a good recovery. However, she did not want to recover, she wanted to die. We would talk in the beam from the light above her bed, dimmed by a blue cloth, about her life. She had been married to an adulterous husband who had ruined her life.

'He was such a handsome man and I loved him so much. But he was never faithful to me.'

Once or twice she gripped my hand and croaked at me, 'Never marry a handsome man, dearie, they will always let you down. '

Sometimes she would try to make me promise not to make the same mistake she had done. It is easy, I suppose to make a promise to a dying woman, but I don't find promises easy to make. This appeared to worry her. As though she were failing in some final duty that might have salvaged some of the worth in her life. Had I promised I would, years later, have broken it anyway. How cross Mrs Robertson would have been. And how wrong she was.

From my time in Alexandra, I was to make the only friend with a patient who was to remain one for many years. She was just sixteen and very beautiful and, one day, was to become the wife of George Melly. She had a bed two from the end of the ward overlooking the Thames. On quiet nights, she kept me talking as long as I could afford. She never treated me as though I were a nurse—always like a friend. Later on, I was to become godmother to her first son who, when he grew up, tragically became a victim of the drug scene. We had lost touch by then, but I wrote to her and she replied very quickly. Her life had sped away from mine but the contact was still there. Now I sometimes see photographs of her in the paper, looking almost unchanged from the face that talked with such animation from the pillow so long ago. She, more than any of the others, was a reflection of my memories of Alexandra, where I had emerged completely from the troughs of frustration and frenzy that had symbolised Charity.

9

It was while I was on night duty on Charity that I first witnessed that most dreaded nursing experience, namely death. I had seen many people in the various stages of dying. I had come very close to seeing death in my first week on a ward. But after that it eluded me for another year. I would have an afternoon or a day off, leaving a patient critically ill, and would return to a bed enveloped in clean linen and know that the worst had occurred. But the longer it went on without seeing death, the more I dreaded the first time.

One evening I went on duty expecting to find the quiet ward I had left the night before. But the fact that Night Sister was present meant that dire happenings had, or were about to happen. She picked me out the moment I arrived.

'Have you ever seen anyone dead, Nurse Coventry,' she said, addressing the top of my cap.

After such a comparatively long time in a hospital, it was likely that I had done so. As I had not, I shook my head, feeling my heart flutter like the wings of a dying bird.

'Come along, then,' she said briskly and went towards the side ward, where she was about to initiate me in the final service ever given to the human body.

On the bed lay a large, uneven mass covered with a sheet. As we approached I was told that she had been an emergency admission that evening and had suffered a subarachnoid haemorrhage (a form of stroke) earlier in the day. She had died soon after admission. With that, Night Sister drew back the sheet. The horror of mixed emotions I felt on the sight of that first dead body, I have never forgotten. She was not a patient I had known. I had never seen her living expressions. Nor was aware of the background to her life—as I was to be aware, with all those people I saw die afterwards. But the sheer physical shock of that first death was the worst.

Her face was contorted with a distress that combined mental

agony with profound physical suffering. The one seeming to engrave its deep, black lines on the other. As a result, her face had set in a mask of bitter grief. A grief rent by the suddenness of unexpected catastrophe that had hit her with a mighty blast, not sparing even her deepest and most secret self. It was all mirrored there in her expression. Those of us who saw her were not spared the turmoil of knowing what losing her life had cost her in every way.

The law of averages caught up with me soon afterwards and I was shortly to witness numerous people die. Once, when I had just finished doing Last Offices with a rather voluptuous Nightingale, she turned to me and said, 'Do you realise that we have just done something that someone will one day do for us?'

That comment speared a temporary but gaping hole in my confidence. How appalling, I thought, that some day my death might cause a young nurse the same feelings of insecurity and disbelief that every person's death caused me.

My reasoning powers were never able to tackle my emotions when it came to death. Only very rarely did I accept that death had a good side—that it gave as well as taking away. Perhaps it was because my first experience had blinded me to the fact that most people looked peaceful after death. It was not until thirty years later, when I nearly died myself, that I could envisage a situation where the reality of life can slip into the reality of death, with an ease which I would not have believed possible, providing that pain is absent. That often much the larger share of the suffering is borne by those left behind who care. In those days I felt there was hardly an occasion when death was justified. These feelings became particularly fierce when it happened to the young.

One of the young I was to see die was a girl of fifteen who was called April. April was a vivid, blonde, lark of a girl who had an exceptionally large goitre on her neck. She was miserable about that. It ruined her appearance, she thought, and she hadn't even had a boyfriend yet. Even her girlfriends were put off by it and thought it disgusting. She couldn't live with it another second. In spite of this, she was always full of optimism and breezy cheerfulness, with only the occasional doubt entering her mind.

'What about the scar, though, will it be awful, will it put everyone off? But it will be less terrible than having a great bladder of a neck and popping out eyes, won't it?' She tinkled with laughter at the no-choice situation she was in.

And so April went on, day and night, chattering away; excited, fearful, joyous and anxious. Up and down, until the day of her operation eventually arrived. I was given the job of preparing her for it (it was another time when I was on night duty). I got her ready just before I went off duty, as she was the first on the operating list in the morning. She questioned me in tumbling words all the time, begging for reassurance. I gave it to her in good faith. I was certain that she would be all right. I then gave her a premedication and I noticed that she was settling down drowsily as I was going off duty. She waved to me across the ward.

'Next time you see me, I will have a proper neck,' she said.

I replied that she would indeed.

The next time I saw her was the following night. I knew as I went on duty that something terrible had happened to her. Her bed was screened and appeared to be lit up by searchlights as people swarmed hither and thither around her. Her face was ashen white and pouring with sweat as she lay propped up on a mountain of pillows. She was quite unconscious but her open eyes stared loopily at the ceiling as though they saw something in it that hypnotized them, and could not draw them away. Like that, with her goitre gone and a neat dressing over her wound, I thought how pretty she looked; that what was happening could not be happening. I willed her to live. To be able to see herself as she had longed to look. She musn't die now—not now. Then I became part of the fringe of activity around her. The ward sister stayed on duty into the night and did not leave her side.

She lived for another hour, two, three—I have forgotten. It seemed an eternity of struggle. During that time there was not a flicker from her face of consciousness. But inside I felt she was fighting, second by second. Had she not been so young and determined she would probably have died hours before. She would not let go of life until, very suddenly, her heart stopped. In the vacuum of silence that followed, those of. us around her bed looked at one another in bleak and bitter awareness. Certainly, it was the most poignant moment of my training.

What had happened to her? She had, apparently, recovered well from the initial stages of the operation but then, late in the afternoon, had gone into a 'thyroid crisis'. As a result of which, her heart had started to fibrillate and she had lost consciousness. From that moment it seemed to have been a losing battle.

As I cleared up her bed, I found myself cursing that she should have had such rotten luck. I had known that there was more risk with a girl of her age. But she had had all the necessary preparations for her operation. She should have come through it—I had known plenty of women who had. What had that lovely girl done to deserve death at fifteen? I remembered how I had told her that, of course, she would be all right. Why had I said it? Partly because that is what she wanted me to say but also because I did feel sure. She was the first person I saw die after an operation and, in the whole four years, I only saw three people die this way. The young generally recovered like magic. But her death was a turning point for me. It made me look at every patient afterwards, however young or trivial their complaints, with eyes that prepared me for their mortality.

Another death that was to affect me very much was that of a policeman called Arthur who was a patient in George Ward. I saw many deaths in George, as there were a number of patients with heart and circulatory problems—for which there are more advanced treatments now, but then recovery had more to do with those architects of healing, time and rest.

Arthur had come into hospital as a result of a coronary thrombosis and had, for at least a week, been on what we called 'complete rest'. This meant he was allowed to do nothing for himself at all. He was the sort of person to whom these limitations must have come very hard but, like all the best of men, he managed to adapt and even used his inertia to his advantage and became one of the central characters in the ward. His particular form of magnetism was that he had a profound ability to make the best out of the worst. I never heard him complain—not once. The doctors, the sister, the nurses, the ward and even the food (however unlikely this might seem), all were perfect. He seemed completely devoid of self interest and was always bothering about the nurses backs as they lifted him, their feet as they slogged about, their complexions if they looked off colour.

'You look tired today, Nurse Coventry. Isn't it time for a day off?' He was a delightful man.

In due course he made the recovery that had been expected. Nevertheless, no chances were taken with him and he stayed in hospital for a protracted period of about five weeks. During that time the patients on either side of him both died. One from a heart attack and the other following a complex operation on his duodenum, which was very unexpected and harrowing. Arthur did not mention the word omen, but these deaths must have shaken him. However he remained his old, cheerful self and, wary as I had become of certainties, it did seem as though he had made a complete recovery. As the day of his discharge approached I remember thinking how flat and dull the ward would be without him.

But on the very day of his discharge, we lost him. His death was happening as I was coming on duty to a weekend work period when I was due to be in charge of the ward. I immediately saw the screens ominously placed round his bed and rushed to his side. He looked at me with tears in his eyes and begged me to try to get his wife to him in time. But his wife was not at home. She, poor woman, had already left for the hospital with a suitcase of clothes to fetch him home. So, doing the only thing I could think of, I tore downstairs and paced around the door that I thought she would come in. The minutes dragged by. I felt my sheer desperation might hurry her up. But how could it? To her Arthur was fit and well and eating his breakfast before getting dressed to come home. I believe I felt—no, I am sure I knew—the exact moment Arthur died for my pent up nerves suddenly changed from extreme urgency to the dregs of exhaustion. By the time I saw his wife, I knew it was already too late.

The death of one of the patients next to Arthur, a Mr James, was a cause of much self recrimination on my part. He had also had a coronary and was also on complete rest. He was a man whose character was strangely containerised. His features frozen in a mask, he closely guarded the keys to his heart. He was very conscious but completely unresponsive. He barely spoke, although he could have done. I felt curiously antagonised by this. Easy communion with patients was something I had come to take for granted. Patients who were apparently much sicker than he, were able to gain solace and so much else from those fibre-like bonds between the nursing and the nursed. Remoteness at close quarters I have always found an uneasy truce.

One evening, when he had been in the ward for about a week, I was blanket bathing him with another nurse to help move and lift him. When we had finished and the other nurse had left, I noticed that part of his draw sheet was still rucked under one of his arms. Without thinking, I pulled it straight, without lifting his arm first as I should have done. Instead he lifted it himself and chortled a little as he did so, as he said it tickled him.

I stared at him in amazement. My first feelings were ones of delight. He *could* respond. Then for a flickering moment I felt uneasy. We were reminded all the time that patients at this stage of their recovery must make no effort at all. Then it happened. The laugh guttered out and his mouth fell down the sides of his face. All the creases of life dissolved before my eyes as though they were melted. It was the first and only time I watched a heart stop on a sixpence. Terrified I took his pulse but I could not feel it. A houseman nearby came to my stricken beckonings and spent some time trying to resuscitate him but to no avail.

Very shaken I told him my story and he replied, 'I don't suppose it made any difference. Mr James seemed to have lost all interest in life. So can you imagine a better or happier way to die than laughing?'

In a way, perhaps he was right. Laughing, lying under a pastel blue sky in a hayfield, embracing, riding a horse, dancing, eating fruits de mer, listening to Liszt's Psalm XIII, 'Lord How Long', or Brahms's Violin Concerto, or, better still, singing in Faure's immortally beautiful Requiem. To die in happiness must be the thing. And particularly for Mr James who had been so unhappy till that moment. But I began to feel uneasy again when I had buckled down to the weary business of Last Offices. Whatever the doctor had said and whatever crutch to my conscience he had given me, I privately thought it was my fault.

Later on it settled down into being a complex. Firstly, I knew that I had let down the hospital. I had broken a rule with the most dire results. Whatever wrong. I may have done to Mr James, I had done a similar one to St Thomas's. Our responsibilities to the hospital were equal to those to the patient. To let down the latter was to let down the former. Secondly I believed that I had found in myself a person who was less caring with those patients she liked less. Thirdly, it was wrong that because I was, and still am, so affected by charm in others, that I should feel irritations when it was absent in a patient. Admittedly, those feelings were rare—so rare that they would hardly have counted if the Mr James incident had not happened. But it did happen. I have always felt very sorry that it should have.

There was one other death that I had felt very personally involved in. Her name was Polly and she was twenty nine years old—quite an accountable age to me then but of course it is nothing. She had metasteses of an original breast cancer, but we did not get the impression that she really knew what was wrong with her.

When I first saw her she was as thin as a little sprig of sticks. Yet her spirit was as fresh as if her flesh hadn't almost vanished away. Her face was ravishingly pretty, even in its emaciated, jaundiced state, and was carefully made up each day. Her hair, beautifully cut and combed, stood up thick and rich in colour from her head. She had a deep voice and laugh that crackled a little and had the ring of an actress about it. There was about her, in general, a special brand of glitter which made one, when talking to her, quite unaware of the grotesque hand that fate had laid on her.

The main reason for this was that she was in love. Her fiancé, who was considerably older than herself and totally devoted to her, spent all the time he could at her bedside, as together they planned the future. He was having a house built for her in the countryside, where she would go when she was better. Bob had also bought her a lovely engagement ring, carefully made so that the stone did not slip under her hand. He drenched her table, locker and windowsill with flowers and brought in little delicacies for her to eat, and spent long, long hours talking to her about the years they were going to spend together that lay ahead.

Never by word or glimmer of emotion, did Bob give away what he had been told. And never, either, did Polly cast one doubt on the fact that she would get well and become his wife. Even when she was actually dying, an event so protracted it seemed to take weeks to come to an end, she talked about the certainties of her living future. I wrote to my mother, 'Polly is only expected to live two more weeks'. But somehow she made it four.

She died just before Christmas when I had gone off duty. Perhaps it was just my imagination, but so many people seemed to die round Christmas.

10

By the time I had reached my second Christmas, I had worked for seven sisters including Night Sister.

Nightingale sisters must have been a legend long before I went to St Thomas's. Dressed so that they stood out like beacons in their Prussian blue, white spotted dresses—stiffly collared and cuffed and crowned with those unmistakable fan shaped caps with their fluffy trimmings and bows under their chins—they looked like hospital field marshals. And they were. They bustled, they focused, they dominated, they organized. They seemed to wrap their wards around them, like some great cloak in which they could feel every fibre of its lining against their skin. The sisters *were* the wards. To me, they were indistinguishable one from the other.

All the sisters had their magnetism. Some as fine as gossamer. Others as substantial as iron. There were multiple barriers round them that, as student nurses, one simply did not cross. The sisters straightened our spines, mobilized us, sharpened our courage and even seemed to find some magic serum to increase our brain power. They taught us that the whole spectrum of nursing was an art as much as a science. Indeed it was more of an art. No women could have known more about the gardening of nurses and the caring of patients than they did.

As the sisters were known by the names of their wards and departments, I was to learn few of their surnames, let alone their first names. What was personal to them, what made them individuals was irrelevant to their purpose. The less one knew about the other side of them, the greater was their strength. All of us grew to admire their extraordinary durability in the face of anything at all. In the end I must have worked for nearly a score of them and, although I had my favourites, I do not remember feeling dislike for any. Fear, yes. I felt that on several occasions and they could also evoke in their subordinates shame and nervousness, sometimes to the point of tears—and once to a nurse on night duty, unconsciousness—but this never led to mutiny in the ranks, you did what you were told and that was that.

The sister's reputations went before them. When changing wards, it was an important issue to find out, at the very least, the outline of the sister's character and what she expected of her staff. A few major gaffs in the first days on a ward could play havoc with one's confidence. Each sister had her own ideas about nursing, her own rules and regulations. Some even appeared to run their wards like a separate state, with long years of experience laying the foundations of all their philosophies. This did not mean it was like going to another hospital. The sisters were all Nightingales so there were only the fine lines of deviation in detail. Nevertheless, they all had minds of their own and this could make quite a difference to the style of one's duties and behaviour when working for them. So a little research made a smoother passage of entry.

There were three really tough sisters whose reputations spread around the Nightingale grapevine. I had heard about these sisters in the dining room before I worked for any of them. In the end, I was to work for all three, so am in a position to give one worm's eye view of what it was like.

One of them was Sister Christian who was in charge of a women's medical ward and was a formidable woman. With Sister Christian, I started with a tiny advantage as she liked nurses who had fair hair and blue eyes—in fact exactly the opposite to herself—and I was lucky enough to be born with both of these. The nurses whose looks she liked did get on with her better—everyone said the same. Once I remember her turning on a Nightingale, who obviously did not come into this category—after she had dropped and broken a porringer—saying, 'Don't just stand there nurse, with your face like a mug in a soap dish, clear the mess up'.

Nevertheless, Sister Christian was one of the best nurses I have ever come across, and one of the hardest working. No job was too menial for her, no hours too long. More than any other sister I can see her now, carefully removing her cuffs, rolling up her sleeves—and on with the job. She moved round the ward like a panther, enormously fast and soundlessly too (she must have worn rubber soles).

She was fairly short but well built with strong arms that had in them the power and expertise to lift women of whatever weight and cumbersomeness, with a facility bordering on the unreal.

With the patients she was an angel. No other sister treated them with more gentle deference, or kindness, or intimate understanding of their needs. Every person was a special case that required her most solicitous attention. She involved herself in every aspect of their recovery as though each one's future affected her personally (this, of course, was true of all the sisters, but with Sister Christian it was particularly noticeable because she was such an expert at the art of detail). She seemed to be a woman of immense intelligence with a quicksilver brain, edged with the finest margins of sensitivity. For the nurses she had her code. The healthy were there to serve the sick and that's all they were there for. She hated slackness, halfheartedness, slowness in others. With her it was sink or swim.

One of the most memorable features, was her sense of humour which gave even her darker moods their silver linings. Occasionally, when we were standing forlornly admonished, I would glance at her and detect some beams of light that moved in her eyes. I can never remember her laughing outright, at least no more than a chuckle. But she had a deeper awareness of the oddities in our sometimes strange profession than many another sister. Providing one did not answer back—mercy upon us—or barely struggle to vindicate a misdeed, forgiveness came rapidly in its wake. Often in the form of a joke that was as dry as dust. Only one matter made working for her a little disappointing, and that was that she allowed the probationers very little free rein. When I was appointed to Christian, I had just come from City, where the opportunities for experience seemed to be great. So to go back to the restrictions of my earliest ward days did, at times, make the work boring and monotonous. Yet, because of the character of its central woman, the ward itself was anything but that. I do not suppose that a single event even of a trivial nature happened in the environs of her ward without her thorough knowledge of it.

At the end of it all, she was kind enough to give me the best report I was ever to have. But I felt that it was mostly due to the way she mobilized her staff that she was able in the end to praise them.

Sister Beatrice was another who ran her ward with brilliance and in whose rather remote forbearance many nurses felt afraid. I never worked on Beatrice Ward so my association with her came when, for a period, she was Night Sister. That was enough to teach me about the calibre of her brain and her competence as a nurse. As well as the impeccable standards she expected of every nurse that came within her vision.

I was in charge of a ward for a period when she was Night Sister. So, when she appeared in the middle of the night to do her routine rounds, I would accompany her around the ward giving her up-to-date details of the progress of each patient. I do not know how many patients there were in St Thomas's at any one time, but Sister Beatrice had certainly done her homework on each and every one of them. Sometimes, as I made my way along the ward with her, stopping at the bottom of each bed to give her the name, diagnosis, treatment and condition of every person without recourse to notes, I found that I hesitated (to hesitate was a very unNightingale thing to do). The darkness seemed to confuse the bed positionings, and, with nothing but a sleeping lump for identification, fear would pluck the prepared recitation right out of my head. This was particularly true when I had just returned from nights off. There might have been a slight shuffle round of the patients, new admissions, discharges and so forth. In most cases my memory came to my rescue, as the rustle of impatience beside me began to stir.

But on one occasion, no amount of examining of that inert and faceless mound could put a name to it. Those agonizing seconds (for seconds were all that they were) were broken, as a tight and crisp voiced Sister Beatrice gave me the information that I was supposed to give her.

'This is Mrs Togdale. She has a gastric ulcer and is being treated with rest, diet and X, Y and Z drugs. She has had a good day and is expected to be discharged next week.'

Shame drenched me as we passed to the next bed. Not another word of chastisement did she utter because she had already said them all. I looked at the marble profile silhouetted by her torch and realised that it hid any expression that might have relaxed me. After that, on every issue that had a question mark over it, I was conscious of my failings. Perhaps she, of them all, was the sister who maintained the most rigid and inflexible attitude to her subordinates. She was the supreme nursing artist who, I am sure, had gathered together more knowledge of sick people and how to make them well than most experienced doctors. After a while, appreciating this to its full extent—her wonderful competence during a night crisis was one example—I found I liked and admired her in a way that it is easy to like and admire those who have absolute talent at whatever they do.

The third sister who was considered fearsome—but less frightening than the other two—was my old friend Sister City. Hers is the laugh I can remember the best. Hers the voice rippling across the keys. Hers that special brand of savoir faire and almost girlish spirits that made her show more of herself as an individual than any other sister I worked for. But that I was frightened of her there is no doubt. She was the only sister who, at times, I felt was unreasonable and unfair and fairness was something that burst for recognition inside me and was, I felt, a very strong factor in the Nightingale make up. It balanced its tight lines of training with the strongest undercurrent of justice—at least I felt it did.

With Sister City, however, there were moments when I doubted this and I almost had to lash my tongue to my jaw to prevent myself from answering back. I realise now, though, that she was the exception that proved the rule. Her character had numerous surfaces and each reflected a dimension of herself. But underneath she was a Nightingale as deeply entrenched as any.

In those days my own temperament had been smoothed by those of my tolerant and equitable parents and nurtured in a moderately small school, whose originality and imagination had given ample opportunity for me to develop my particular interests, so my school days had been very happy ones. My time in City, though, provided me with an electric current of awareness about the realities of life which was to stand me in good stead when, later, I became a mother, when I discovered that my patience with my own children was decidedly limited.

My daughter at ten defined the matter. 'Mummy, you are sort of hard-soft.'

Wasn't that exactly what Sister City had been? In one of my letters to my mother I had written about her like this:

> 'I bought an earthenware vase for the ward this morning with which Sister City was thrilled—she nearly embraced me. She paid me out of ward funds.'

I have no means of knowing why I performed this service for her. No doubt she had commissioned me to do so. But her responsiveness to such matters explained why I, and so many others, enjoyed working on her ward. Yet, it was, perhaps, not until those early years of rearing my children that I felt I had reached a formal understanding with the past. Sister City treated her ward like her home, her patients like her dearest friends and relations who had come to stay, and her nurses like her children.

The other sisters I worked for remain, as those three do, substance not shadows. I recall expressions, characteristics, smiles, bees-in-the-bonnet. Most of them stayed on their wards for years. Once a nurse had accepted the honour of an appointment as a ward sister, I am sure she regarded it as her life's work. If it had been possible, I think some of them would have liked to die in harness. During my whole four years in the hospital, there was only one change that I knew of. And that came after the retirement of Sister Nuffield. I did not work on Nuffield until she had left it, but I can remember what she looked like. In the geography of her face and in her upright bearing was writ large the personality that people talked about.

But whatever the sisters were like, I really preferred it when they were off duty. When they were there, I felt I was always looking over my shoulder. That my every move was connected, as though by electric cables, to their actions, needs and requirements. They also, because of what they were, managed to extract a level of awareness from their subordinates that I, for one, found it difficult to sustain at the necessary height all the time. Standards did not go down in their absence. It was just that the nurses became less sister-orientated and conscious. Besides, their second-in-command, the charge nurses, were always superb stand-ins. They combined the confidence of the sisters and doctors with a calm, elastic, discreet and balanced one with the student nurses. We were closer to them. They were the middlewomen; the pivots—the dock leaves to the ward's stings—vital, it seemed to me, to the harmony of ward life. All the charge nurses I knew had a rich, humane quality and, dressed as they were in their dusty-blue dresses, beautifully cut so they looked so trim, they seemed elemental to the ward system. Had I been asked, I would not have thought it possible that a ward could function properly without them. Yet, when I visit other hospitals, I am always looking for charge nurses who are not there.

The charge nurses played as important a part in teaching and training us as the sisters themselves.

11

When I first went to St Thomas's, I was given a schedule of nursing duties that I was to be taught by the sisters, marked with my name, the date of entry into the Preliminary Training School and that of the Nightingale Home. Underneath this a paragraph runs thus:

> 'The Sister, as she teaches the nursing points mentioned in the left hand column, is kindly requested to mark the same in the column descriptive of her ward—Surgical, Medical etc. One stroke is to signify that a Nurse has been shown, but is not proficient in detail: an X to mean that the nurse has been taught and is proficient in the same. The Sister who placed an X will insert her initials in the right hand column.'

The schedule was divided into seventeen sections, including that of special work at the bottom, and these included some hundred and twenty nine different duties of which I was to be shown and become proficient in a hundred and two. The sisters had graced my schedule with one hundred and thirty five sets of initials.

The majority of the nursing duties itemized on the schedule are eternal and will never change. But many must now be obsolete and a few, perhaps, were even then. I noticed several ways of reducing fever that I was never to come across For instance, the inclusion of leeches I found fascinating. I was never to see a leech there but a Nightingale friend of mine, who went on to be a sister elsewhere, confirms that they are still occasionally used on severe bruising. I was not taught that, however, and if I had a bruise myself, I would rather keep a bruise than have a leech remove it for me.

Apart from our training by the ward and department sisters and those on the theatres, we had our annual lectures from a redoubtable and unforgettable figure of a Sister Tutor who stood like a life force at the centre of the Nightingale Training School. All the nurses came under her tutorage during our annual lecture periods. But for the rest of our training we must nearly all have had different mentors. Few, if any, followed exactly the same progression of wards and departments. My selection was both contrasting and effective. I have a strong slovenly streak in my character but even the most gentle of the sisters imbued the Nightingale essence of excellence, thoroughness, perfection into the granules of my make up. There was no short fall you were allowed.

The Nightingale Training School stood on the sturdy foundations of supreme example. I can see Sister Christian now, making a bed. Pumping and pummelling the pillows, twisting them this way and that. Placing some vertically, some horizontally, some in a pyramid, tailoring them exactly to individual needs. Bedmaking was, as indeed was every other duty or action, an art form to them. Then I can remember Sister Elizabeth brushing the flimsy white threads of a ninety year old woman's hair, dividing it at the back and then, lovingly and carefully plaiting it to the end. Attaching first two elastic bands and then two blue satin ribbons. Attention to appearance was given a natural importance in our training. So it came to pass that I learnt to wash and arrange hair in the way patients wanted. Fixed up with pins, in nets, in rolls, buns and bunches and frequently, with the old, just plaits.

We were taught in faultless detail all the mechanics of nursing. Take lifting. Always, we had dinned into our heads, spare the back—take the weight on the shoulders, the hips, the legs, the arms. Never the back. In fact we were taught that taking any weight on the back is wrong and that we must always bend our knees when lifting up an object—however trivial and light—from the floor. As a result I never strained myself, even when obliged to lift some of the gargantuan men patients I was to nurse and doing the other sturdy duties expected of us. I cannot remember any Nightingales suffering such injuries. We were simply taught how to avoid it and, had it happened, it would have been our fault.

The sisters expected that everything we did should reach the same standards they set themselves. Therefore anything imperfectly done, had to be re-done. Those long hours spent perfecting the art of filling water pillows—a ghost in all Nightingales lives—were standards expected in all our duties and treatments. Very rarely were we allowed to patch up work that was not considered by the sisters to be exemplary. It was a question of starting again from the beginning.

For instance, the abdominal bandage that we made ourselves at the Manor House and which took quite a long time to adjust and fix properly could, if the sisters disliked our handiwork, be flipped open—bang. Then the arduous stretching and gripping and pinning was renewed.

Back at the beginning of my training I used to wonder if I would ever get anything right. It had produced in me exactly the same feeling as when I was a child playing snakes and ladders. The rich happiness of landing on and mounting a golden ladder. Then the horror of the jaws of the red snakes, that a three on the dice could send one plunging down. However, by my second year, I had almost rid myself of the peculiar inferiority complex that not attaining perfection, when it is essential, can produce. Quite apart from the fact that I had the harvest of a years experience, the continual polish of the training had produced wily tentacles, as well as compulsive habits. All of which went a long way to protect a once exceedingly exposed vulnerability.

There was much that was taught by the sisters that altered a whole pattern of thinking or behaviour, in the same way that actors say they take a part into their own lives. Mostly my nursing self went on and off with my uniform. But some things were impossible to shed. Like the way we were taught to be acutely observant—having eyes all round our heads, in our fingers, even in our feet. Even now I am far more observant of details in people, in surroundings, in events than I would have been without the awareness shaken into me by the sisters.

I can hear Sister Christian now, 'Well, did you notice it? Or did you not? You must know?'

Procrastination, fumblings with excuses, were red rags to sister bulls, particularly to her. Later on there came praise.

'She is quite intelligent and observant, in spite of her long lashes,' she once said to a staff nurse who kindly passed the information on to me.

I was surprised how that little blessing of mixed honours pleased me. In general I do not think that praise played much part in encouraging betterment, except in ward reports. In fact they probably thought it was a false premise on which to base a sound training, You got your confidence other ways.

In general, I think our awareness was sharpened even finer than I have made it seem. On entering a ward I was conscious that my nerves went on sentry duty, so that I was not just expected to be observant but to trace the arts of anticipation right back to their first beginnings. Our sister tutor often used to say, 'prophylaxis is better than cure'. This became our constant refrain. So much of our training was based on the supposition of prevention. All the numerous and devious paths that illness can take and the understanding of the various calamities that could be attendant on even the simplest treatments if the proper precautions were not taken, became second nature and still are.

Another lesson which was endemic in our training was that of economy. Every article that we used that could be recycled was. From bottles that held the blood, through the syringes and needles, bandages, masks, rubber gloves and tubes, in fact every particle of our equipment in daily usage that could be washed, boiled, scrubbed or sterilized and remain in one piece at the end of it—was used again. Nor was there any question that we could be profligate, even so. Take the question of linen, for instance. The key to the linen cupboard was as carefully guarded by the sister in charge of the ward as that of the drugs cupboard. Sheets were changed when there was a need to change them and the draw sheets, that were tucked over them, were so long that they had the double advantage that they could be used twice. This did not mean that the beds ever looked other than perfect but no sister would have dreamt of changing a sheet simply because the patient had had it on the bed for a couple of days. Maybe it was a legacy of the war or just our times but not a sheet did the state pay to be washed that was not necessary.

Not only were we taught about material economy but also about that of effort. Never go around with your hands empty, nurses, so they taught us. With the distances that we covered, it was very good advice. If we were designated to take something somewhere, there was nearly always something else that could be brought back. Trips to meals often involved fetching drugs from the dispensary or taking syringe needles to be sharpened. Wastage of any sort seemed almost like a vice. We ourselves folded the dressings for the sterilizer drums, sewed and mended when mending was possible. We were also encouraged and drilled in being quiet, quiet, quiet: voices low, silent swiftness, never clumsy. Courtesy and good manners, too, came very high on their list of priorities. A whole control of the person in its nursing capacity seemed to be what they aimed at.

But most important of all, was the attitude we were taught to take to the patients. It had been part of Florence Nightingale's teaching that patients were guests and that every aspect of their welfare mattered as much as any other, since recovery depended so much on the level of morale. Hence the importance we put on the patients' appearances; the accountability and neatness of their belongings; the brightness and freshness of their flowers. It was why little tots of whisky or brandy were often slipped into the men's milk at night if they wanted it. And why the big wards always had an atmosphere that made those in the side wards want to get back into them. Also, we were encouraged to let the patients confide in us their worries and problems so that these could be reported to the sister. If she could not rectify these herself, in all probability the almoner could. It was a whole understanding of the part the mind and spirit took in recovery. The aim of the Nightingale training was to create the best possible circumstances and environment in which this could happen.

As to what I eventually achieved on the wards in proficiency 'X's, they did gradually gather momentum as ward succeeded ward. With each sister giving her opinions—which often differed from one another—as to what I was proficient at. Examining it now, there does seem to be one anomalous feature. While there are a host of 'X's against many of the more complex treatments, some of the easiest day to day nursing activities never merited a cross for proficiency. Apparently I never became proficient at the care of patients' hands and feet, or at lifting them. Not one sister saw fit to honour me in those simple tasks that were performed numerous times automatically every day. Perhaps my contemporaries found the same. The sisters, I am sure, had their reasons.

12

One sister I particularly liked and for whom I worked in early 1953 was Sister Mothercraft. Hers was the outpatient department chosen for me and had I known, in advance, what she was like—young, friendly and kind—and what happened in Mothercraft, I would have chosen to go there for myself. It was situated in the basement but had a cosy ambience and the whole ethos of looking at life at its beginnings I found exciting and, in a way, escapist. Here was a different world and one to which I adjusted at every level.

However, this was not what I thought on my first day there. That morning there was a clinic for young married women who were infertile and included a girl still in her teens who, after three months of marriage, had been unable to consummate it. The treatment was a simple one and, after a demonstration, I was left on my own to perform it. But simple or not, that treatment caused that girl much distress. As a result, though deeply buried inside, so did it me. I felt our invisible emotions (for she said nothing) were joined along a great reef and I learnt something about quite a different sort of courage than I had had to face before. Nevertheless, she returned at regular intervals for further treatment until the goal was accomplished, and she reported that her marriage had become a normal one. I felt jubilant about that and had a personal sense of achievement. Most patients were cured by shared responsibilities. But not that girl, she had been my responsibility.

At the time, I thought that her case might be quite an unusual one. Although I already knew something about the straight mechanics of love making, I was almost totally ignorant of the physiology of it. I had only a sketchy idea about the functioning of erectile tissue and I did not know a Bartholin gland from a bar of soap. My experience with Mr Rock had given me a good idea of what was required from the man's point of view. But until treating that young patient I had had no conception of the difficulties encountered by some women in crossing the first sexual hurdle. I knew that when I was kissed by a man that strange and delicious changes seemed to happen to my body. But did not necessarily identify these as a preparation for the final act of love. My knowledge in this sphere was astonishingly limited.

Did none of this come out in our lectures? Maybe it did later on—I suspect in rather a circumspect way and not until after I had worked in Mothercraft. Certainly, we were taught in painstaking detail all the anatomy and physiology of reproduction. There on the blackboard would be the sturdy, headless uterus with its stumps of legs (the cervix), its flailing arms and tendrils of fingers ready to catch the wayward ovum which, if it were lucky, would be fertilised on its journey to the uterus and imbed itself in its lining. We were taught what happened during every minute of the menstrual cycle, whether conception happened or not.

But of how love making was made easy and enjoyable I knew almost nothing. My family did not discuss it with me—I would have been very embarrassed if they had—and of course, one was taught nothing at school then. But young people, or anyway those I knew, never discussed it in detail amongst themselves either. Even when a friend of mine had been on honeymoon, she just reported that sex was rather a messy, pongy business.

'One needs a sense of humour all the time to get through it'.

Without asking any questions, I envisaged all the stories about taking a little towel to keep blood off the sheets and left it at that. To ask someone what they knew about sex was rather like asking them how much money they had. You just didn't do it.

Strangely, though, my earliest instruction in sex came very early indeed. Even before my curiosity had been aroused sufficiently to be more then mildly interested. I had watched mounting cows and locked together insects and our spaniel was always wrapping himself round my legs but I connected it with affection no more, no less. Then 'the truth' arrived.

When I was seven I went to a school in Scotland where, in the same class as my ten year old sister, was a doctor's daughter who no doubt had access to all sorts of books and charts unobtainable to the rest of us. From these she discovered what she believed to be the facts of life. Elated with her success, she spread the word to her enthralled classmates, including my sister—who promptly told me. Being a little doubtful about part of the information that seemed a little dubious, even to my seven year old mind, I accosted my mother with the subject when she was, appropriately enough, picking gooseberries.

She said, very quietly, 'It's something like that. You are too young to understand now but you will when you are older.'

Her answer satisfied me far more than she can have imagined. Suddenly I felt immensely grown up. I knew how babies were started and I was sure none of my friends did.

When I was a little older, I chanced upon Voltaire's *Candide* and was totally gripped by its revelations. These, and all the other facts, I gradually learnt, I came upon by accident, not through investigation. One of my chance pieces of information came on the back stairs at school when I was thirteen. I can so well remember hearing two senior girls discussing marriage.

'Everyone does it on their wedding night,' crowed one of them with the smugness of having found out first.

Do they, I thought in horror. They must be so exhausted after the wedding service and everything. Why do they have to do it *so soon*? But another fact had been chalked up on my mental blackboard. They do it on their wedding night.

Well, on that first day in Mothercraft, I had proof that they all did not. Although I had no proof that they had not tried. I just knew that romance and wedded bliss were not automatically the same thing, as much of what one read in those days would have had one believe. I think that really I was a very romantic person. Mothercraft not only taught me much but brought me down to earth with a thud.

It was there that I learnt far more about the mysteries of life than I was likely to learn in any other way. Clinical it was but fascinating. Within days I was allowed to examine pregnant women and listen to the foetal heartbeat, and stand beside doctors pontificating about the advisability of intercourse during pregnancy or immediately after it.

'Apart from your health, breast feeding is not the foolproof contraceptive that it is made out to be. It is better to refrain from inter-course for at least six weeks after the birth.'

One woman thought it unlikely that her husband would stand for rationing in this matter. Hygiene? Another baby? He'd not be bothered. Nor was he. After she had given birth in a ward upstairs, he almost had to be restrained from getting into bed with her. Then there were the occasional confidences to us, as though we were practiced women of the world, used to hearing about bedroom frolics. Up in the wards, male Cockney lack of reserve was taken for granted. But, in Mothercraft, I came across much of the young female variety of it too.

All that apart, I was entranced by what I learnt about the development of babies from conception. The impersonal 'in utero' names—embryo and foetus—that sounded to me anything but really living, were unveiled to reveal a baby whose heart had been beating on the twenty fifth day of its life. Who had minute internal organs when it was less than the size of a thumbnail. Perfectly shaped hands and feet at twelve weeks, and who was practicing breathing, crying, and swallowing in those early weeks before there was any visible sign of its presence. It was not possible for me to learn such facts and not be moved. The depth to which my imagination explored them added another dimension to my months in Mothercraft. I was hungry for information and never became sated with it: there was always more to learn.

And then, after the babies were born, they were brought back to be weighed, immunized and test fed if necessary. I had never handled such tiny babies before. How reassuring they were with their downy heads, their flaccid limbs, their animal-like reactions, their peepings and peerings from under hooded lids, and the way they fitted like water pillows into the curve of your neck, the crook of your arm, anywhere you wanted to put them. Even the negative aspects about them, such as their gaping furies and putrid nappies made me love them with a love that I had always felt for very young creatures.

To prepare the mothers for this whole cycle of experiences, there was Mother's Club. Amongst the numerous advices they received, they were shown—and allowed to experiment with—the use of the mask for gas and air. The nurses were also shown this and given a good whiff of nitrous oxide as well. This set another Nightingale and myself off laughing irrationally and foolishly for nearly an hour. Yet, years later, when I sucked in that gas during my first difficult labour, it did not have any effect. Not a laugh did it produce nor a pain did it hinder. I remained washed around in oceans of agony. I wondered if any of our mothers had fared better. Or if, like me, it had just been a useful instrument in which to bury silent screams.

In those Mothercraft weeks, I was lucky enough to witness little that went wrong in pregnancy. I can remember none of the women aborting. However, in the wards, I had seen two cases of spontaneous abortion.

The first was in its very early stages and the baby was not much bigger than a thimble. Almost transparent from lack of substance and, naturally enough, quite inert.

The second baby, though, was about sixteen weeks developed. Had grown to about eight or ten inches in length and looked, even at my brief first glance, quite perfect. It was handed to me in a large porringer, apparently dead, with a cloth thrown over the top, for disposal. In the sluice, I removed the cloth, in spite of fearful misgivings, to inspect it. I noticed immediately that it was a boy. Further swift reckoning saw that, anyway externally, he was apparently normal. Exquisitely formed in miniature, being slender and fragile, without all the padding that babies get later in pregnancy to make them look younger, not older. I took all this in in less than a few seconds. For then, to my horror, he appeared to move as though in a long, silent, death shudder. There was no apparent breathing, just a tremulous shaking that finished almost as soon as it had begun.

My instantaneous reaction was to pick him up, wrap him in a blanket and rush into the ward to see if he could be revived. But hard logic followed. No baby of such immaturity and weighing so little had ever been able to survive and this one's battle to do so was ending. He had become quite still, although his arms which had been curled up on his chest now fell to his side where they lay with the palms facing upwards. I made a tiny cross on his forehead. Then very carefully covered him again.

I left him alone in the sluice and went across to the bathroom, feeling shocked and sick. I could not bring myself to dispose of that child as though he had been a cyst or growth. Not the budding, swelling spirit of human life that nature had intended. I sat rooted to a chair, thinking about life and how it works its devious patterns. There grew in me a compulsive curiosity to know what that baby would have been like. What he might have achieved, looked like, loved.

There grew simultaneously in me, both a fear and a hatred of abortion, which would have made nursing an impossibility for me after it became legal to induce it. At least with spontaneous abortion, one had the meagre comfort that Mother Nature often disposed early that which, in some way, was not perfect but, I imagine, the sight of forcible induction of perfect foetuses must crack many a tougher nursing skull than mine. This was not a consideration then but comforting the mother was. So I pulled myself together and went back to her bedside.

I found her brave and resolute. After having undergone an experience which seemed to her as painful and prolonged longed as a full-blown labour, she had already got out her comb and was doing her hair. She had not been told any details about the baby because she had not asked. But she had been told that there was no reason to suppose that she could not have another child. Always the hope for the future. That was what counted.

13

Under a cloak of smog left by December, 1953 had trudged in. Those smog years in which so many of our winters in the fifties were shrouded, have left numerous memories: powder puff lights from the street lamps—suspended in mid air; lack of movement—the stillness; onerous silence—the cloying smell. And the sense of suffocation. The smog seemed particularly bad around our coil of the Thames—its familiar landmarks gone and no world amidst the smog but its own.

To escape it on every occasion that I could, I made tracks for the country. This had been made easier since my father had retired from the navy and my parents had settled near Winchester. To go there I only had to cross the short distance between St Thomas's and Waterloo, so this I regularly did. By the time the train had reached Woking, the sun was escaping from its ochre filter and, by Fleet, it was free.

Those times I spent with my parents at Winchester became the backdrop to my nursing life. My parents had turned their new house into a haven of comfort, beauty, nourishment and love. Their belongings settled around them, as they always had in their numerous previous houses, with natural ease. My mother complemented them with a profusion of plants that flourished under her tender administrations—she hated to see a plant die.

In the garden she uprooted the hedges that had trussed its acres into lots and filled the resulting borders with about a thousand rose bushes; all carefully chosen so that colours did not split, but flowed together. Roses abounded everywhere. They swung up the front of the house, showered over the trellises, clung to the roof of the potting shed, and nestled round the door of the apple house. Apart from the roses, her herbaceous border swarmed with colour in the August sunshine—a mass of harmonious shapes. Long borders of shrubs edged and divided the garden where edging and dividing was necessary.

In the background, vegetables grew unobtrusively and obediently, exactly as they should. The fruitcage was annually covered with a net to prevent the birds from pecking at the harvest of strawberries, raspberries, gooseberries and redcurrants, At the back of the garden, orchards of apple and cherry trees gave the family most of the fruit it needed. And a long walk of hazel nut trees and a walnut tree, most of its nuts.

Often, on my visits there, I would help my parents with the mammoth task they had taken on in middle life with a garden that size. (This was not all they did by any means: both of them quickly became involved with local activities in the village and Winchester.) But sometimes I would lie on the lawn under a cherry tree, with carpets of daffodils in the orchards nearby, and peruse the sky, and fill my being with the essence of what my parents had created. Never could there have been a quicker way to shed nursing tensions than there was there.

I very rarely went out with men friends, or any friends for that matter, from that house. It was not a house one went out from, it was a house that brought people in. My parents' visitors' book was filled with the names of friends who had come to enjoy their hospitality. My mother's invisible labours making their stay so effortless, and my father's knowledge, humour and tolerance igniting much of the conversation and laughter. It was the happiest house that any young girl could have dreamt of having. It often took some major event, such as a St Thomas's Ball, an invitation to the Derby or the Café de Paris to keep me away from it. Any man in my life had to compete with the tug of a totally happy home—my parents never rowed, any discord was patched up with invisible mending. So unless I was really interested, I was always happier there.

Because of this, most of the other venues that had filled the gap in my parents' absence in Scotland were abandoned with a few exceptions. One was the house of a close friend in Surrey, where a cadet friend of hers from Sandhurst and his chums would crack us about on motorbikes or in Passion Wagons. Another was the house of an uncle of mine in Essex, where life was lived as though nothing had changed for a hundred years. My uncles house—still one of my favourites of all the houses I have known—was a beautifully proportioned Georgian mansion, set in a garden of majestic trees and expansive lawns. Surrounded by thousands sands of acres of farmland, it had not altered its style since I had known it as a baby. I—or frequently we, since my whole family gravitated there—often went for a special occasion such as a fete, a shoot or a ball. Sometimes we just went there because we loved it.

On arrival at the nearest station, a car would be waiting with the familiar face of the chauffeur, who had worked for my uncle since I could remember. He would tuck a rug around my knees and drive in a gentle, unhurried manner along the roads and lanes to the house. My uncle and aunt were always in the hall to greet me and, close behind, cousins and frenzied dogs. My suitcase, with its rather more carefully selected garments than those I took home, would be whisked away by swift and silent hands to be unpacked in my bedroom. That was always the beginning of a stay at a house that I shall call Gumley Hall.

In the morning my shoes arrived clean outside my bedroom door (I have never been a great one for cleaning shoes myself—even at St Thomas's I found it an awful chore—but I liked having them cleaned for me). Then a tray of early morning tea arrived at eight and at nine a gong went for breakfast. Those breakfasts at Gumley remain memories that will always linger, as they stung the morning appetite and made it difficult not to gorge oneself. On one sideboard there were three or four silver dishes that contained an assortment of immaculately cooked eggs and bacon, kidneys, fluffy scrambled eggs, kedgeree and other delicious items, as well as boiled eggs every day. There was another sideboard with porridge and cornflakes, with large jugs of fresh farm milk and bowls of cream to ladle over them. On a third sideboard there were bowls of fruit, a haunch of ham and always a newly baked loaf with a crackling crust and a soft moist centre. But best of all, from my point of view, there was a large honey brown Norwegian cheese, which one slivered with a special implement from the top. Thin slices of this, warm and melting with butter on top of a wodge of the steaming bread, was the most perfect taste that had ever entered my mouth.

I would battle with my weakened will to stop myself from getting up from my chair to fetch a second, third or even fourth slice of this delectable concoction. And always turned my back on the toast and the homemade marmalade.

By the time breakfast came to an end I was full to the brim and had eaten quite enough to last me all day, but there were three course lunches at one. And proper teas with scones, sandwiches, biscuits and cakes at four, before the formal dinner in the evening. At dinner we all changed into evening dress (dinner jackets for the men and long dresses for the women) and had one or two glasses of sherry before dinner—never the hard stuff. A gong announced our dinner, as it did for all meals except tea, and we sat down to a procession of courses accompanied by exquisite hocks and clarets. The older gents then had their port, while the rest of us withdrew to the billiard room to play cards and games. I doubt if my uncle ever saw a television programme, let alone had a set in the house.

Apart from all this eating, the days were spent walking the dogs, riding and, in winter, hunting. Playing tennis, helping pick apples in the orchards (my uncle's estate made its own cider) and driving around in a pony trap. A world as leisurely and remote from my one in London as any world could have been.

On Sunday mornings we all attended church and sat in the family chapel. Here, part of the stained glass window showed a scene of my dying great grandmother, amongst her grieving family. Staring at this would occupy much of my time, in between singing the hymns in my rather loud voice. My uncle and aunt had their own means of speeding up the service. At the beginning of the sermon, my uncle carefully released his gold fob watch from his waistcoat pocket and would open it with a loud click. Ten minutes later he would snap it shut to indicate to the vicar that enough was enough. My aunt was equally adept at time and motion. There was a beautiful organ in that church—probably larger and more beautiful than a church of that size would normally accommodate—and the organist would exploit its prowess in largo modulations. To hasten the proceedings, my aunt would gallop along in her strong mezzo soprano, singing sharp, and finish the hymn or psalm half a verse in front of the organist.

There were also other distractions. One of the young choristers was an epileptic. Every Sunday she would have a fit and fall flat on the floor. Then, when it was over, get up and resume her singing. This seemed to be a Sunday ritual and no harm seemed to come to her. Another chorister spent much of his time bouncing his cross off his surplice, as though it were a trampoline, and it would shoot into the air to the amusement of the other choristers. Just behind the chapel was a door in the wall underneath the nearest window. It had once admitted those parishioners who had failed to attend church the week before. There they were made to stand in disgrace for the whole service. This had not been practiced for many hundred years, so it was a long time since the door had been used. I remember as a young child feeling rather superior, sitting separated from the main body of the church in that little chapel, so it probably had induced in me better behaviour than was normal. We were driven to church by Hamlyn, the chauffeur but always, if it were fine, walked back.

For special occasions, such as a ball, the Gumley atmosphere changed from its gently stirred routine into a buzz. The balls were given in the dining room, cleared of its contents for the purpose, and there were house parties for about ten young people, including my cousins, my sister and myself. We decked ourselves in such finery as we possessed and, with white kid gloves up to our armpits and dance cards round our wrists, we were ready for action. The dance cards I found quite a mixed blessing. After a survey of the assembly, I would spy one or two partners I would have chosen for myself but, apart from the male content of the house party who were obliged to dance with us whether they wanted to or not, my dance card seemed to fill up with those whom I had not noticed at all.

At those balls I was loath to admit I was a nurse. To many people, I felt, nurses were a cause of social unease—particularly, perhaps to men.

'Gracious, this woman knows every inch of my body inside out. She knows where all my nerves join up, what my glands do or should do. She can monitor the signs of masculinity. Every pimple she can analyze and put down to something odious about me. If I cough, her respiratory protractor will get going and if I'm sick she won't think its just because I'm drunk.'

If there were one reason that might have stopped me from becoming a nurse, it was an awareness of the embarrassment some people might feel, meeting a named connoisseur on bodily functions, however part-formed the knowledge, or unripe the experience. So I used to pray that I wouldn't be asked what I did. It was often too much to hope for.

The first partner to put the question to me, let out such a braying laugh that the rest of the assembly might have been forgiven for wanting to share the joke. Another to enquire, was one of those enormous, steel-spined giants, who danced like a poker—with one hand under my armpit and the other gripping one of mine above my head—and steered me backwards around the floor, treading on my dress from time to time, so that it dived over the rim of my boned bust bodice, until eventually he bellowed into the air, 'What do you do?' And bent his head to my mouth to hear my reply. The information I gave him didn't bring any joy to his face and the conversation braked to a halt.

I decided that nurses were obviously social dross and I would admit to being one no more. After that all seemed to go much better. I even, just before the end, managed to attract the attention of the one man whom I had silently selected from those available and can remember much of what he said to me even now. By the time the National Anthem was played, my confidence had been partly restored.

At balls like those in general—where one wasn't taken by an escort but had to be chosen—the spectre of the wall flower always hovered, and the shining white knight never appeared. Then there were times when couples were so squeezed on the dance floor that toes were mortarized under the hefty weights that so frequently trod on them. Hems of dresses were ripped unevenly, providing the perfect noose for the clumsy to fall through. Or one would be crushed into a stiff white shirt and studs. In my early youth I had fed my mind on the Gallic sophistication and portrayal of a ballroom as read about or seen in films—courtly swirlings and balcony tenderness—but the reality never provided a copy of the image.

This did not mean to say that I would have missed them. Nor would I have changed them for what exists now. Or that a place such as. Gumley did not make such a ball exciting, because it did. Everything that happened there was special. It was the one remaining house in my life that, in its lifestyle, represented the closing of an era. It is sold now and turned into. a hotel; its stables flattened, its gravel drive a tarmac mass of sleeping policemen, its gun room a bar, its billiard room a garage. My weekends there (for while I worked in Mothercraft or on night duty, there were weekends to be had) or with my parents at Winchester—or, more in frequently, with my ailing grandfather in Wiltshire, whose unmodernized edifice, secret gardens, teeming moat and tree-filled park, had been the glory of my childhood—not only gave me numerous breaks from the smog, but re-charged all my nursing batteries to the brim. I could not have asked for more.

That period of my training was good in many ways. I had moved to another nurses' home, Cheyne House, on the corner of Royal Hospital Road and Chelsea Embankment, with a direct view onto Albert Bridge. This house was the best liked of the nurses homes by my contemporaries, I was to stay there for much of 1953 and 1954—except when I was on night duty, for which special quieter houses had been designated. Apart from its proximity to my favourite part of London, it was a house with a great deal of style: a large hall, elegant curving staircase and good sized bedrooms, made very light by the size of the windows.

There I was to share a room with another Nightingale friend called Jo, who has become a stayer. Peggy and I, who had been together and shared rooms until the end of our first night duty after Christmas 1952, somehow—I cannot remember why now—had been parted at the beginning of 1953. When we had been probationers, it had not been difficult to arrange to stay together.

By the time we were staff nurses, our different responsibilities spread us far and wide (apart from Hydestyle, the Grosvenor and Waterloo Hospitals were also under the administration of St Thomas's).

Jo was quite a different sort of person to Peggy, but we got on admirably. She was one of those Nightingales with rather an angelic look about her, but was no angel. She had an open frank manner that I found too funny to be rude. Once, after a visit of her family to Cheyne House, she told me that I was not her mother's type, but that her brother had said I was probably the sort of person that grew on one—a comment I felt applied equally to him. Later on, she said to a friend of mine, 'you don't *look* as though you come from Gloucestershire'.

However, we got on well and established a bond that made her say to me one day, 'let's keep in touch when this St Thomas's business is over'. And we have. I think she found the Nightingale training a little sharp for her taste. She left at the end of her four years to become a sister in a nursing home, where the attitudes were more relaxed.

Towards the middle of that year I worked on a men's surgical ward called Nuffield (after its benefactor, Lord Nuffield). By this time the renowned Sister Nuffield had retired and her place had been taken by a young and extremely pretty sister who was later to marry the student I had nursed in City. During my training, many an appealing knot like that was tied. That sister was, I think, only about twenty six when she took up the appointment, and was most sympathetic with us. It would be a long time before she reached the age when the faults of student nurses were incomprehensible, I used to think. Again I was in my favourite setting. A men's surgical ward where humour to pathos was the greater ratio.

I was working on Nuffield at the time of the coronation and was one of the numerous Nightingales lucky enough to be given the day off, so that we could go over to Westminster to watch it. When the king had died the previous year, I remember a deep sadness everywhere. To those of us who had been war children he had meant a great deal. I can still see his little circular wave and remember the way one's heart turned over at the sound of his stutter during his speeches. When he lay in state in Westminster Hall, the queue to pay him homage stretched like a thick, black margin along the embankment, across Lambeth Bridge and back in front of St Thomas's. I joined it in my off duty time and it took three hours till I passed the catafalque. I only just got back on duty in time.

By the time the coronation came round, the atmosphere in the hospital was as lighthearted as it was at Christmas time. Beds seemed to empty as though a wand had been waved over the sick. Where were they all, I thought, as I looked at the smooth parade of unsullied beds. The few patients that remained sat chirpily glued to their headphones determined not to be a nuisance. So hoards of nurses were able to cross the bridge and watch the historic events taking place at Westminster.

I had taken the precaution of asking for the day off in advance and, as this was preceded by a half day, set up camp in Parliament Square the day before. Together with one of the friends in my set, Sue Gregory Smith (later to be drowned, to my sorrow, in a boating accident off the coast of Australia), we made our plans. The skies had their all too frequent June sullenness, so we gathered together as much weatherproofing as we could carry, flasks of hot drinks, sundry edibles and reading matter, and set off in the early afternoon of June 1st to the corner of Whitehall and Parliament Square. The first to arrive on that particular spot, we staked our claim and settled down to wait. By the evening huddled mounds of human forms filled the pavement around us and rain, featherlight, tepid and drenching, began to fall. Sue and I made a tent of her mackintosh by placing two flasks at each end. And then we curled up back to back to keep warm.

I do not remember dozing off once. The chatter-chatter of the sleepless, the slurp of the rain, the machinations of Big Ben, the slushing cars round the corner of Whitehall, the stump of uniformed feet, the rock-icehard pavement engraving our flesh on our bones—not a wink and yet who cared.

In the morning, though, our front row position had been eroded. This we minded. The new arrivals had more muscle power so we found ourselves lodged in about the third row. From there, when the procession arrived, we could just see short, broken images of carriages and regalia as it approached Westminster Abbey. The service was relayed into the Square. Zadok the Priest—Vivat Regina Elizabeth—the glorious Gloria and the Te Deum. Every nerve was on fire, as a torrent of bells exploded forth. When the procession returned, we had a direct view into the state coach of a winged smile, a dark flash of curls, an incandescent skin and heaped, purple crown. It was all worth it. We stayed hooraying and jumping about on the balls of our feet until the last clamping of horses' hooves, the last inching car, the last balanced motorbike, the last band and banner, salute and stride; the last of anything that passed had gone. Then we gathered up the remnants of our camp from the pavement and, with a few belated gleams of sunshine playing darts round the spires of the Houses of Parliament, we recrossed the bridge back to St Thomas's.

Sue was living in Gassiot House (the nurse's home next to the hospital) at the time, so we went to her room and flopped down on her. We were exhilarated but barely recognizable. Our hair hung seaweedlike around the sepia skin and black cavities of our faces. Our eyes were rimmed in red and furrows burrowed deep into our brows. In spite of our youth it took two days to fully rejuvenate ourselves, and about the same time for the hospital to get back into normal harness again.

Following the coronation there was a hectic month in Nuffield and then I took the first holiday I had had since I started my training. I went with a very spirited Nightingale called Patricia, with whom I had worked on Elizabeth, for two weeks to Guernsey.

We set off from the airport at Eastleigh in Hampshire which must, at the time, have been as antiquated as any in England. The terminal had the bare knuckles of an out-of-date railway station and the runway was a hairy looking field with not a slab of concrete to be seen anywhere. Our homely Dakota sat at the end of the field, revving up its engines for a quarter of an hour or so. First one, then the other, then the one, then the second, on and on—the plane seeming to inhale and exhale with each warm-up. Till, eventually, it bumbled off down the field. I did not really expect it to leave the ground and was delighted when it did.

Those early flights did, at least, have style, The air hostesses were effusive in their concerns and duties and had, within minutes, our aperitifs racing in our blood streams. Only a short time later they had served the lunch—steaming, immaculately arranged, four-course. The pilot on the intercom continually soothed and explained. There was a noticeable lack of pressure and, although I think we discussed the possibility of our imminent deaths much of the way there, we arrived in Guernsey replete and relaxed.

We stayed at a smart boarding house for 12/6d a night, half board, and spent our days walking or going in buses to the beaches and playing tennis in between times. We were lucky to have picked, apparently, the only fine fortnight of the summer, so spent much time lying baking on rocks, giving ourselves second degree burns (in those days there were five degrees of burns). No one thought in the fifties that there was much art in sunbathing. We just turned ourselves over, like toast, when the sun had got too hot. As a result of which, we lay in fire-beds for a couple of nights, and my chest continued to peel for nearly six months. Apart from that everything went perfectly.

I don't remember too well what we did with our evenings, but we spent much time chatting with our hosts. They were both entranced with Patricia and said she reminded them of Ava Gardner (so as not to leave me out, I was like Marylin Monroe). There were few young men around or I think they would have come our way as Patricia was as attractive to men as a candle is to moths. Not only was she very pretty but she had that most dependable attribute, confidence—which I most noticeably lacked. Only recently has my teenage son given me a rundown on the subtle allure of the confident girl. So now I have it firsthand from a young man I can trust.

It was not just lack of confidence I suffered from. I was also very particular. Most of the young men I met I found unattractive for one reason or another. A far larger proportion of them were that to me than, with such merits as I had, I could afford if I were to establish a good relationship with anyone. Most of my set at St Thomas's had 'steadies' or were engaged. And Patricia was about to land a dashing catch and had another in the pipeline just in case (the latter eventually claiming her), as well as a plethora of anxious or virile attendants, who adored her, to fill in the gaps. In contrast, my love life had been a rocky mixture of one night try-outs or erratic meetings due, generally, to my standoffishness.

Yet I was still not prepared to compromise. I had recoiling memories of a blind date who had taken me to the Colony Restaurant in Berkley Square—then a most fashionable seminightclub, with a dance floor half the size of a boxing ring. Here I had been wrapped around in a shuffling embrace for dance after dance by a man whose touch had made me feel sick, but whom I had dared not refuse because I knew how much it was costing him. Patricia had none of those sort of hangups. She just loved men per se and reaped the rewards with a host of male slaves. There was one man on Guernsey who had met her 'somewhere' and followed her around the beach all one day, but, apart from that, we spent our time on our own. I still have some lovely, hydrangea-strewn photographs to bear witness to the pleasure we had.

During that autumn, the final stages of the film 'Genevieve' were filmed outside the hospital. I was coming out of one of the side entrances to catch a bus back to Cheyne House and walked straight into the film set.

A megaphone instructed those of us hovering on the pavement to move across the road and, shortly afterwards, down Lambeth Palace Road came an old, yellow car with an air force type in tweeds (the then unknown to me Kenneth More) at the wheel, accompanied by the elegant Kay Kendal and, in the back, the sad looking St Bernard, Susie. I had never watched a film being made before, so spent my off duty fascinated by the motoring madness that developed before my eyes. Not just with that car, but with the smaller, dilapidated Genevieve. We were quite used to the old crocks annual trip across Westminster Bridge on their way to Brighton. But this was different. Never then did I envisage that this film would become a classic and would immortalize that stretch of

Lambeth Palace Road that has now passed into history. Yet, somehow, the director managed to keep any evidence of its hospital background out of sight. On a normal day, doctors and nurses used to walk up and down those railings so frequently that it would have seemed impossible to have cut them out. But not a sign of a uniform or a starched white coat is to be seen. Nevertheless that film contained a significant part of my past.

That winter we were plunged back into smog again. One day I was trying to make my way over Westminster Bridge to the underground when all visibility stopped. I could not even see my foot. A feeling of panic ensued. What if I could not find my way back? It took me nearly twenty minutes to feel my way round various sets of railings and buildings, till I found the hospital entrance. No nightmare I have had has ever been more weird or alarming than that experience. The smog had seeped into the hospital too. The downstairs corridor was thick with it and in the wards one felt as though one was in caves. So many people died that shouldn't have. It was not just the effect on the body, it was the effect on the soul. It killed hope, it stopped visitors from coming, it was dark and lonely and evil. The day it eventually lifted was one of miraculous happiness. I wrote some verse to celebrate it.

> The motion of traffic begins to break
> The surface of sound, infinitessimally
> At first: the trams clunk, the buses purr,
> At last a hoot, a brake, a roar, though a
> Little muted still—still covered in a cloth.
>
> Buildings move upwards into a scene,
> Amid light that tries to scatter the remnant
> Of smokey clogs of fog into dazzling particles,
> Above barges smouldering still in latticed lines,
> And cargo that bows down again upon its knees.
>
> Water turns its back once more on
> Boats that pass, and peels

Its rim with little crusts of froth
Which eyes that peer can see. The hard disc of
Big Ben's face beams aloft and shouts again with glee.

And Westminster Bridge again joins
Our eastern bank to its western approaches,
And has shed its girdle of grim
Air paste to return in liquid symmetry
To span our loin of the Thames.

14

Up to now I have made little mention of all the men around the hospital. Although we student nurses had eyed them from a distance from the beginning, we had had little contact with them. Except those we had nursed—and it was surprising how many St Thomas's men came into the wards as patients—or unless we had found an opening into the students ranks. But after we had gained some seniority as staff nurses and had been in charge of a ward, even for a short length of time, this began to change.

In truth, I never really got to know the consultants. Those times when I was in charge—on night duty, in the evenings and at the weekends—they were never in sight. The set programming of their ward visits always synchronized with the sister's or charge nurse's duty period. So the consultants remained remote—people one studied as from an observatory.

From those observations, I found them a remarkably impressive array of men. Most of them were large and broad with big voices and manners, as they moved around in their stiff white coats with never a mark upon them. During their rounds, the sisters appeared to guard them like well trained dogs. If, for any reason, it was necessary to interrupt those rounds, we were obliged to stand behind the hallowed knot of consultant, registrar, houseman and sister—our hands behind our backs until we were noticed when there was a temporary lull in the beams of communication that glanced on silvery tongues between them. The sisters would turn their heads with that slightly defensive look of people who are critically short of time, to enquire what it was we wanted. Many of them hardly needed to open their mouths to convey their replies. From the scrolls of their expressions appeared a flick of a smile, a lift of an eyebrow, a moving glint in an eye. And that was enough. I always felt like a trespasser, even when an emergency was at hand. I had become so very conscious of the levels of importance in a ward and which way the balance could be tipped. The consultants were more important than most trivial emergencies, and one's coping barometers registered exactly the moment for a little more boldness. During these intercessions the consultants stayed glaze-eyed and boot-faced.

Aloof as the consultants might have been with us, they had a bond with the sisters that seemed like a yoke: the mercurial understandings between them, the stripling jokes and the sister's exact measurements of each one's temperament and likely demands. I often felt that, underneath the veneer—however much they might have conveyed the opposite impression—the sisters often had the last word. Had the consultants been lesser men than they were, it might have been more than that. But we all believed in them absolutely and loyalty to them was second nature. Now, if I ever hear people be critical of treatment they have received from a name that was a symbol of our Nightingale times, I jump to his defence, as I would for a member of my own family.

In the arranged hierarchy, the consultants immediate subordinates with whom we had much more contact were called the R.A.S. and R.A.P. (respectively, Resident Assistant Surgeon and Resident Assistant Physician). When I was working at St Thomas's I thought that these appointments automatically occurred in all hospitals. But I have never come across their like since. Those selected for these positions came from the ranks of the senior registrars and lived on the spot in College House. They were ready and available as superintendents of out-of-hours emergencies that were beyond the experience of the housemen. As well as being much in evidence during the day so, along with the housemen, theirs were the faces to which one became most accustomed.

The appointment was for two years and, inevitably, an extremely responsible one. The men chosen for it did look special. Of no importance to their function in the hospital, but interesting to me, was that the men selected for these high posts seemed to be endowed with remarkably good looks. Chance is a funny thing, but the R.A.S.s and R.A.P.s I remember were dreamboats. I had nursed one R.A.S. in my second year who had been such a perfect specimen of manhood physically that, had he been a man outside the hospital, I would certainly have done my best to attract him. But as a registrar of such importance he was, of course, quite out of my range. There was plenty of matching going on in the hospital but, nearly always, people selected those of equivalent standing, which was perfectly understandable. But it made it different from those relationships one made outside. There was no question, either, that there could have developed with him, the slightly jokey, cheeky relationship common with the student patients. That R.A.S. had the kind of charm that wore Venetian blinds.

The housemen, of course, were the doctors who became our kindred spirits. And what respect I had for those indomitable men. As the general factotums of their respective consultants, they were appointed for one year—except for casualty that was for six months. During that year, they appeared at all times of day or night, their short white jackets flying at their sides, to struggle with blocked canulars during blood transfusions, to scribble up drugs, get case histories; examine, listen, thump chests, bang knees and then report, report, report to their seniors. Heaven knows, I have seen men work, but I have never seen men work like they did for a pittance of a few hundred pounds a year.

One of their problems must have been the way the hospital was arranged. St Thomas's—being a Victorian hospital in every sense of the word—was divided so that all the men's wards were in its southerly half and nearly all the women's wards to the northerly end. This meant that if a consultant had a patient in Clayton Ward, which was at the top of the men's block at one end of the hospital, and another patient in Beatrice at the top of the women's at the other—very likely, as it happens, as they were both surgical wards—there was a considerable distance to cross between the two. Nor was it just that. Only the first floor wards were linked by a corridor (City was the only ward on the ground floor), so two flights of stairs had to be descended and mounted as well. No use of lifts, remember.

The extra burden this must have put on all the doctors in the hospital at that time, particularly the hard pressed housemen, was brought back to me when, a few yeas ago I was a patient in the modern Charing Cross Hospital. There I was put in a unisex ward. We had separate partitions, of course, but under the same ceiling. I took some time to accustom myself to this. A Portuguese maid was always rushing in to adjust my nightdress, for she did not feel that I made decent viewing for the Arab who, during his daily constitutional, passed the end of my bed. But inspite of this, I thought how much easier it must be to have their patients so conveniently arranged. And I felt pity again for our troopers of the fifties who, because of the wide segregations, must have slogged round miles in a week.

I suppose one of the factors influencing some young girls about to embark on a nursing training could be the fact that so many men are around. Yet I have to admit that, as a person with rather questionable reasons for training to be a nurse anyway, it had not influenced me. In fact before I went to St Thomas's I had no preconceived designs on the men. And when I got there I did not change my mind. As far as the students were concerned—although I had had my minor flirtation with the fellow in City—I found them, en masse, rather glum and heavy, as they lumbered round the wards with their slightly hangdog expressions and toothbrush haircuts, and I could not detect traces of the kind of spark that would have made them interesting. I cannot remember whether many of my contemporaries were overwhelmed by their allure either. I think they were the last subject that we would discuss in the dining room. Men, yes, but students…well.

They, of course, started in very unfavourable circumstances compared with ourselves. Theorizing for years at their desks and carving up corpses in their laboratories, before they took their first steps into the wards to examine patients. Ten weeks of theorizing at the Manor House seemed long enough to us. Had we had three years of skeletons and smelly chemicals and the rest, real patients would have looked as unreal to us as they appeared to look to many of them.

I always got the impression that the sisters did not have much time for them. Sometimes sweeping them off the brown lockers by the beds—on which they sat curled up with their pads taking notes from the patients—if a treatment needed doing. And generally not looking filled with joy at their appearance on the ward. A few sisters qualified their rules to them.

The old Sister Nuffield was known to have said, 'There are three things you may not do on my ward. Sit on the beds, spill blood on the sheets or interfere with my nurses. Remember that, and we shall get on.'

Many of them must have had occasion to be intimidated by the nursing staff as well. They did not have the superiority of a white coat either, as. they do now. A student was a student—blazer and bags, no more, no less.

However, all can change and did. There was an annual hospital athletics meeting at their sports ground in Cobham, where nurses and students were selected from wards to compete against one another. In the summer I had worked in Christian, another nurse and myself were chosen, along with a couple of fleet-footed students, to run in the relay race, which we duly won. This was celebrated with beer and photographs all round.

Then, at Christmas time, the students, put on a revue to which nurses flocked if they could get off duty. These shows were generally very funny. Peggy and I attended one together and our raucous bellowing at the punch lines and sometimes murky humour turned a few heads. There was a fancy song about the alimentary tract, with a refrain concerning nitrogenous waste. And another about that platlet gobbler, the spleen. There was also a gentle, lyrical song about Rutland of which I can remember only one verse.

Rutland, glorious Rutland, breezy bracing Rutland
It's a little patch of sunlight in the gloom,
But we fear that we may lose it
If a cow gets in and chews it,
But we'll live and die in Rutland
If there's room.

As everyone knows, a political cow did get into Rutland and chew it and those who feared they would lose it, did. How that song came back to me when the beautiful structure of our counties was decimated.

Those shows were put on at St Thomas's House where most of the students lived and where, also, there were occasional dances. These were spirited affairs and, I seem to remember, took place mostly in the dark. There were rough, old brown sofas round the edges of the room and these gradually filled up with romantic couples. At one dance I had a gently simmering relationship with rather a shy student who, to my slight disappointment, behaved with old fashioned decorum.

Had I been asked, I would have automatically connected medical students with sport, revue and passion. But I was surprised by their displays of art. In 1953 there was an exhibition of photography in the hospital, so talented that there might have been budding Cartier Bressons in their midst. At the time I was becoming keen on photography myself. My parents had given me an old bags and bellows camera which, antiquated as it was, had taken some good photographs for me. But, for some reason, I barely used it at St Thomas's, which was a pity, as our area was full of pulsating stills, as some of those remarkable photographs showed.

At that stage I knew few of the students well but there were many that I had come to recognize. One of these, was a fellow I had met at a ball at Gumley. I had first spotted him during a students' round on City. He had given me a little bow, his Etonian tie falling out of his blazor. He stood out from the other students because he was smooth to the point of silk. While many students appeared a little woolly, Duncan—as I shall call him—had tresses that clung to his head. His cardinal cuffs and creases, to say nothing of his molecular charm, made me wonder if such looks might not be a liability in a G.P. If there were an emergency in the night, would William Holden x 3 be the answer, however skilled? He did not, moreover, waste his looks. In his spare time he became a model and clinched the second top woman model of the day as his girlfriend. I never got to know Duncan well although he has haphazardly turned up in my life several times since.

My first real outing with some students came when one of them had laid their hands on a boat and a few of us Nightingales were invited to join them, and went off down the Thames on a pub crawl. When we arrived at the Prospect of Whitby, I excelled myself by missing my footing and falling into the water. I was wearing a cotton dress with large strawberries on it, which proceeded to congeal round my legs—hardly a propitious way to start an outing. Nevertheless, it caused considerable amusement. What with that and the barley wine burning down our throats, we all lit up and the evening, lurching from one ancient pub to another, embellished in a sensation of shifting back hundreds of years in time, was a huge success. After that there followed many other pub evenings.

'To hell with poverty,' once raged a student I rather liked.

For many of them it did seen to be a case of pubs and easy pickings. Although, eventually, I had some lovely outings with them. There was a knees' up at the Lyceum and, a little later with the same chap, a visit to 'Salad Days' that was showing in the Strand. There was a trip to Covent Garden (not the Gods), to see Weber's 'Der Freischutz' and to hear the new Australian singer, Joan Sutherland. There were some delectable meals in bistros in Fulham, candlelit across rough tables or gay gingham cloths. And there was one seven course meal at the Dorchester. That was on 'grandad'. Grandad was a laird from Scotland who sat wrapped in tartan in his suite on the top floor. He had quite a crisp Scotch brogue that he buried in his chin, and he drank neat whisky from a huge tumbler. He also spent a great deal on his grandchildren, who brought their friends in for refreshment. Recalling those outings and the money spent—girls rarely offered a farthing towards their outings in those days—all behaved like gentlemen and did not expect more than the most trivial favours in return.

However, I did, once, fall very much in love. This was with another student I nursed—this time on Arthur Ward. This student, whom I shall call Peter, had just finished his pre-wards period, so I had never seen him before. By the time I met him in 1954 I was a senior staff nurse, so worth a second glance. Which was how his first words came to me.

'You stand looking at,' he said as I was pouring some potions from the drug trolley.

I feebly replied, 'at what?'.

He did not bother to explain such an obvious miscomprehension but repeated those four words again and a third time. The penny then dropped and I felt vulnerable. I thought he might have marked me out as a possible target and then deliberately tried to test me. A swift understanding meant I was immune—confusion meant I was not. Certainly, I was always susceptible to any compliments. If people told me something pleasant about myself I wanted to believe them. I certainly wanted to believe Peter.

However, after such a display, I did not expect any further interest in me, and forecast that he would turn his attention to other nurses. But, for some reason, he persevered. He would sit in his bed, his knees drawn up under the bedclothes, with a book or newspaper balanced against them, often puffing at his pipe, and look up at me from under a flap of brown hair, his eyes creased in charm and his mouth smiling at one side or the other, rarely—except when he laughed—at both together. As a senior staff nurse, it was easy to find legitimate time and reasons to talk to him, and the more we talked the better I liked him.

Apart from his obvious attractions, he was also very intelligent. He was supposed to be taking important exams at that time but his illness—he had a serious condition—had prevented it. So an examiner just came in to talk to him. I don't think he was even given a proper oral. He was just asked a few questions and that was decided to be enough. His previous work had obviously given clear indications of what he was capable. I do not imagine such a method of passing a student through an exam had been used often in the hospital before—if at all. But Peter was not usual. He was most unusual, and that was what was so disturbing about him. He did not try to impress with any of his qualities; he had a casual, almost lazy way of attracting one's attention, but no man I have ever known had more skill at it. So whatever resistance I might have had, quickly wilted away and I began to feel the liquid transports of love.

All my life I had been ready for that moment. Right from the time when I was a thirteen year old and had, every Sunday, gone to even-song at my local church in the hopes of catching a glimpse of a boy I had fixed my feelings upon, I had been on the threshold of falling in love, but the appropriate man had never quite materialized (hardly surprising, after what I have said about myself) so there had always been a flaw between a man and my loving him. Now there was no flaw. Peter was the personification of the ideal lover.

He had a unique way of going to the heart of a woman. He would catch me unawares. He would use words like 'exquisite' and senten-ces like 'God put a lot of thought into making you'. One never felt that he was using his subtleties to manipulate feeling, although I suppose he might have been. He also had a masterly way of apply-ing his agile mind to train and realise my thoughts, before they found their way into words. This was another form of flattery but I did not see it as such. Simply that he was making our affinity act as a bridge for him to cross. He was twenty four. I suspect that he had had plenty of experience with women and understood them, and the peculiar arithmetical complexity of their makeups—like a man who was a genius at maths. But I did not recognize that then. I thought it was his love for me that made him so eloquent and ir-resistible. And that must, at least, have been part of it.

Yet, even as I got deeper and deeper into the mire of love, I was still able to stand back and look at it. I saw it, and so did he, as a love affair. Not as something that would last and become marriage. There were at least two reasons for this. The first was that he al-ready had an involvement. This was understandable. There was a well known book at that time called *The Unfair Sex* by Nina Farewell and it had some salient lines in it. One passage went something like this:

> Men do not spring into existence the moment you meet them. They have not been waiting for you to cross their paths. They have already lived a whole life and the more attractive and interesting the man, the more attractive and interesting the life.

That was true, I thought wryly. Moreover, it put exactly the girdle round my expectations of it that I felt I wanted, because of the second reason.

This was our different backgrounds. His was more intellectual; mine more traditional. Now that would be a positive advantage and, from my point of view, it might not have mattered then, but for my very close relationship with my parents. Up till then they had been the most important factor in my life. I could not visualize marrying anyone who could not accept them exactly as they were or enjoy fitting into their beautifully organized and civilized, if somewhat narrow, existence. My worst nightmare would have come true with the experience of a friend of mine who, having married very young a man she hardly knew, was told by her husband early in her marriage that he did not like her parents or want to see them. Perhaps this had always been the main cause of my ultra cautiousness.

As far as Peter was concerned, he fulfilled that side of me that my parents knew less about. My love of art and music. My growing interest, since I became a nurse, in psychology and social history. Subjects I never laboured at home, because we spoke of different things. But Peter brought factors of which I had been quite unconscious to the surface. It seems strange now, loving him as I did, that I could have been so cold-blooded about it. To believe it was possible to develop a relationship like that, and then abandon it. However, I had no experience at all with which to compare it.

But Peter did, and he knew it could not last. Even his nickname for me had impermanence in it. But against all this, I still could not put a limitation on it in my mind. I did not want it to end. I wanted it to go on as it was.

And how was that? The reason we managed to build up such a close relationship, with him lying in bed and us both being under the constant gaze of the rest of the ward staff—to say nothing of the patients, doctors, visitors et al—might have had something to do with the fact that all staff members who were patients were given that little bit of extra attention, which was accepted as normal. I could also find additional times to talk to him. In the early morning, after I had finished the drug round, there was normally time to slip behind his screens for a few minutes after he had washed himself.

Likewise in the evening. There was nothing suspicious about those rendezvous—but they gave us an opportunity to relax and chat naturally. For weeks this went on, as he was in the ward for a long time—from March 27th to June 10th—so we had what seemed like an eternity to discover what we liked about one another. For the type of relationship it had to be, in some ways it was too long.

During that time he had a serious operation and with it, (except in the fundamental nursing way, which I found quite difficult in view of my emotional tie) the communication between us temporarily stopped.. He was very ill for several days and had to have some nasty treatments. I hated to watch the way his face lost its expressions and became flat with resignation. It both worried and hurt me to see him like that. I also realised that I had become an ordinary nurse. A person to bathe, feed, soothe, brush and tend. But not to love, other than in a clinical way.

This produced in me a feeling of absurd suspension. As though I was in the middle of a tank of water, but could not come up or go down. For, whereas he was quite emotionally detached during that period, I was even more deeply involved. Suffering for him, as one suffers for any sick person one loves. Just before the operation he had had a time of heady euphoria, which I think hid a deep anxiety. Now he was fighting his way through his recovery in his own measured steps. Although I do not think he had expected to die, he was far too clever not to have examined the possibility. As such, he knew he had to conserve every ounce of energy to get better.

And he did get better. Slowly and surely he emerged from the chrysalis of his post-operative weakness and lethargy. After the first week his mood began to soar and burst back into life. During that recovering phase, we became closer than we had ever been before. My diary of that year does not give his operation date so I cannot remember how many post operative weeks we had together. But there were enough of them to get me to the brink of wondering whether I could ever do without him.

After his discharge, he was sent down to Hydestyle to convalesce. When five weeks had passed, he was allowed some freedom. So we had our first evenings out together. The initial occasion was particularly memorable. At last, we had shaken off our fetters and were free. Those fetters has included the daily boredom of our hospital garments. He had never seen me out of my uniform before or I, him, out of his pyjamas. Or, to put it more accurately, in a suit with a tie. I can remember exactly the clothes we both wore and the spot on Brompton Road where we met. We had dinner at 'La Vache à la Cave' (long since vanished) behind Harrods, and I can remember only one other meal in my life—many years later in a restaurant close by—that was as emotionally charged as that one.

A week later we had a pure night together at Guildford ('Yes,' I replied to my mother, when she anxiously asked whether it would be *two* rooms). During the afternoon we ambled along the banks of the river and sat for hours in solitude by its edge—the pleasure of being quite alone together was almost unbearably sweet. In the evening we drank loving cups of wine and laughed until we ached watching the Marx Brothers in 'A Night at the Opera'. When, weeks later, Peter told me he would always treasure memories of that part of our lives we had spent together, I thought the twenty four hours we had spent at Guildford were the ones he would remember the best. Although we never made love in the way that is taken for granted now, that day was complete in every way without it.

I should have realised that the longer I let it go on, the greater would be the pain when it ended. But I have barely lived my life for a moment in the future. I thought it would just come to an end of its own accord, but, in fact, I continued to see him for months and then, suddenly, without out any real warning, Peter decided to end it. A small, deeply felt, but final note arrived in my locker.

During the time I went out with him, I wrote him a poem which, before he saw it, he was very anxious about. On reading it, however, he seemed relieved. He liked my poem. He even thought I could write. As a result I burst into a torrent of poetry writing. Almost all my free time I wrote poems about love and its quintessential happiness. Although I was to love other men deeper and longer than I loved Peter, and am very happily married, I never, or almost never, recaptured the feelings that he evoked. Winged feet, spiritual effervescence to the point of feather-headedness, bodily energy whose horsepower doubled and seemed unable to tire. A feeling of communion with nature, with people—with every element of human existence that touched my life—that was as finely tuned as it would have been possible to be. Of course, much of this had to do with the constraints put upon our relationship for so long at the beginning, but it also had to do with that indefinable attitude, built into relationships between men and women in those days. Peter was the perfect medium for this.

When it was all over, I realised that one of the facets of his character that was so special and seemed impossible to replace, was that he really liked women as well as, I think, falling in love with them quite easily. With the men I had known up to that time—and this was a cry of many of my friends as well—it was fairly normal, after the first flame of enthusiasm had subsided, to become a shadow to their hobbies. How many of my generation of women spent long, frozen hours sitting on shooting sticks or beside rugby pitches; trod the relentless tees and greens of golf courses up and down the country or were shouted at non stop in yachts? How many of us tried to please our men by swotting up the history of the Incas or the Ming Dynasty, waded through H.L. Mencken, went to lectures on the motorcar manufacturing industry, or the science and culture of world manures? Or sat, night after night, listening to the grumpy, deafening Brünnhilde grinding away on gramophone records? I could not count them. If any young, modern women, with their casual outings and premarital nesting, should pick up these pages and think I am just trying to be funny, they should watch the way that Alan McKim and Ambrose Claverhouse treated their women versus their cars in 'Genevieve'. So when Peter caught me off my guard with his sort of witchcraft, the denouement was inevitable. It was not that he excluded his hobbies but he made certain that you became a willing, nay eager, participant.

The worst aspect of emerging from that lost love affair was how it affected my attitude to other people. Broken hearts are not kind ones. I also found that I had been so mistaken in thinking that people who have been so much loved can be easily replaced; that love can be transcribed. While it had been going on, my confidence had become so inflated that it also, in a way, became reckless. It would not be true to say that future relationships with men were entirely free from pain, but I had learnt my lesson. For none of them produced that feeling of evaporation into nothingness that my break with Peter had.

I only had one other emotional experience with a student—of quite a different sort—which happened just two weeks before I was sent to Arthur.

I was in charge of Christian during night duty. There was a patient who, following a chest infection, was having some matter drained from her pleural cavity. This was done by what was called 'underwater seal intercostal drainage'. Briefly to describe it, a rubber tube came from the area being drained and passed into a heavy bottle, half filled with water, on the floor. The tube was submerged in the water to prevent air passing back into the patient's lungs, causing them to collapse. Every time the water in the bottle was changed, the tube had to be tightly clamped.

One evening a student appeared to monitor the progress of this patient. It was the end of March and the ward was in almost total darkness, relieved only by a few beams of light shed from the shades above those who needed treatment. There was a lull typically felt in those wards when the main lights had just been put out. I was busy adjusting the pillows of one old woman further down the ward when, suddenly, there was a splintering crash, which came from behind my head. In a fragment of a second I realised what had happened. I made off towards that noise faster than I have ever run in my life. As I sped towards that drainage bottle, I saw water begin to flow like a great, black map from under the patient's bed. By the time I reached the clamp on the tube to seal it, there was less than half an inch of water in the glass tube that came from the bottle neck. But it was enough. That was all that was necessary.

The bottle lay in pieces on the floor surrounded by the remains of its contents, the jagged glass like ice broken up in a bath. With deliberate slowness, I picked up the glass, wrapped it up in paper and disposed of it, before fetching another bottle. Mechanically my body worked, although I found shock had made me partially deaf for a time. It might seem to the layman that dramas of this sort are common in hospitals and therefore one learns to live with them. They are not and one does not.

The student, a tall blond, kind man, stood shattered at the foot of the bed. It is quite possible that in the darkness his feet had hit the one weak point on the bottle's side, for those bottles were as tough as any I have known, but living, as we did then, with the breakable had its hazards. One could never take for granted that even the stoutest looking equipment would not one day fall apart.

The student murmured his apologies, so deeply felt that they seemed to stick in his lips. I cannot remember what I felt. Was I sorry for him, cool, detached, indifferent? I feel now that there was not much left in me for any emotions. That had I been able to give him sympathy I would have. But that I didn't. Two weeks later it was spring and I was sent to Arthur.

15

Arthur would have been my favourite ward anyway. Was it just my memory that bathed the spring of 1954 in sunshine that fell in cascades into the wards, brimming them up with warmth? Walking past Chelsea Barracks one glorious morning, I remember the sticky sap on the pavements and the air with tiny jets of warm breezes, moving in slow motion around my head. Happiness at twenty one— if one is happy—does not need any additives. But I had those anyway. The moment I stepped into Arthur, I loved the ward with its second floor position (the first time I'd spent a spring so high up in the hospital) and its lovely atmosphere. I felt my whole training came together there.

Sister Arthur was probably the main reason for this. She was character in its purest sense. She seemed to have absorbed the best experiences of her life which blossomed in her behaviour. She was about 5ft 4in, slim, grey haired, and walked fast and purposefully with her body leaning forward on rather stiff legs. She had a sense of humour like a kaleidoscope that changed colours as it was shaken, and a laugh that bubbled away in her throat with a deep and rich tenor. Her energy was bottomless as was her compassion. She seemed to be born to nurse men—one could not imagine her nursing women—and had a profound rapport with them.

Reasonableness was at the centre of her nature and she corrected her subordinates with a fairness that was definite and which one did not even have to question in one's own mind. Although a little sarcasm was not outside her range, it always came with a twinkle—within the bounds of what all of us knew to be just. She was not a person to make nurses feel nervous but they did mind their Ps and Qs. She was exactly the right person for me in one of my first positions as a senior staff nurse.

Arthur, during the time I was there, had a number of long stay patients (patients seemed to stay in hospital so much longer in those days) and this was another reason to find it such a settled and happy place. Peter, himself, was in the ward for eleven weeks and a few of the others for all the time I was there—which was just over three months. Some of the longer stay patients were at the top of the ward with one of the blue screens round the side of their beds.

Peter was screened like this for some of the time after his operation, but mostly, I think, he preferred the screen down. He was always at the top end of the ward. Opposite him was a screened major, whose eagle eyes detected, or thought they detected, some rather unprofessional behaviour round Peter's bed. In fact, all the nurses liked Peter and probably spoilt him as well—he was so highly spoilable. But the Sherlock Holmes in the major sniffed out me as the favourite and made his own deductions from the discreet methods of communication that Peter and I had established. He reported to Sister Arthur that he did not think that my relationship with Peter was a quite normal nursing one. She, who had probably known the score but chosen to close her eyes to it—as she must have had to do on other occasions, young men and women being what they are—very discreetly took me aside and told me that patients should not be given a chance to surmise emotions that might be under the surface and that I must be more careful.

That was all she said. There was no lecture, no threats, no questions, no dressing down. Never have I felt more humbly corrected or more grateful to anyone for their wisdom and tact and I hope I fully repaid her. I certainly tried to.

However, had the major not been screened from view of the rest of the ward, he might indeed have thought that my relationship with most of the men in the ward was suspicious. Whenever I mentally relate to people as I did with most of those patients in Arthur, I treat them with all the joy they can tap in me. And this often involves touching them when I speak.

One of those special patients there was an old boy we used to call Gaffa. Gaffa was ingrown in Arthur. He was just part of the ward and I could not imagine it, even now, without him. I cannot remember what was wrong with him, as he did not seem to have much treatment, though I must have known all the details of his case history. I was often in charge of the ward and had to make reports.

Anyway, it seems an irrelevance now. Gaffa was just Gaffa, an essential part of Arthur's scenery, chemistry and soul. To look at, he was unique. He had the appearance of an original Santa Claus with a very long, grey beard, a thick white fringe round the dome of his head, and a smile that stretched across his face like the sun—the sun rising, the sun setting and the sun blazing all day. In stature, he was short and fat and cuddly, in not an entirely asexual way. His eyes still gleamed the fireflies of his youth and his face, round and smooth, did not carry a single line of grievance.

For much of the time he would shuffle about the place in his blue hospital dressing gown with a rather amphibian waddle. He was not unlike a human walrus. On occasions, he sounded like one too. He had a laugh as guttural as I have ever heard, and a mumbling speech that could have been any language at all. It was quite irrelevant to our enjoyment of him, whether we understood what he said. He made us laugh anyway. As a result, all the nurses loved him and spoilt him outrageously. Our affection for him was far more noticeable that for anyone else but, because he was old and fat, no one minded. One day I brought in my camera and photographed him in the bathroom and his photograph still laughs at me when I look at it.

I could not have been with Gaffa when he died. I could not have borne it. I had seen so many patients I loved die. There were times when I felt I needed to stuff my apron down my throat to throttle the sobs. But Gaffa would have been the toughest. I hadn't then been tested with the ultimate in grief, (the deaths of one of my babies and my parents, although it was only my mother whom I was with when she died). The grief that is remorseless and takes away everything normal but the power to move. Once I had known that, perhaps Gaffa's death would have seemed tolerable. But to give him Last Offices—no I could not have done it. I do not know when he died but I had left the ward then. The last time I saw him, he was just the same: smiling, happy, goodnatured, solid with life.

Another favourite patient of mine there was a policeman called Dennis. Any number of policemen came into St Thomas's, because of its proximity to Scotland Yard. Dennis was a large, luminous man full of the milk of human kindness. He had had an operation for cancer on his scrotum, although they had, apparently, left him with a small part of his testicles—something they always tried to do. In my earlier life I had had much to do with horses and my knowledge of gelding and how it changed both character and looks made the idea of completely castrating a man, appalling. Unless it was absolutely essential, this was avoided somehow.

Anyway, after his operation, Dennis did not change in any way. A model patient, he was soon back with his arms about our shoulders, filling the ward with his soft, caring character and his round, rich voice. There are few people in my life I have known who were solid goodness. Perhaps there were four, and Dennis was one of them. Just before he was discharged he promised to take me round Scotland Yard. He gave me a telephone number to ring so that he could give me a personally conducted tour. With every intention of taking the matter up, I let it slip—and have regretted it ever since.

Arthur also had its artists. There was a sandy haired chap who whiled away his time drawing pictures. One of these was when I was taking a Sunday service at the central desk and all the other nurses were trilling away at the piano. He had drawn himself at the centre of the picture and was naked (and without screens, it would never have happened!) with a pronounced rib cage, a transfusion going into his nose and a vicious looking woman doctor thumping his patella, whilst he managed to hold his prayer book in spite of all. Underneath he had quoted from *Omar Khayyam:*

> A flask of wine,
> A book of verse,
> And thou...

One of the less happy patients was a gentle, quiet man who had been admitted to the hospital unaware of what was wrong with him. So he was stunned to learn that he had syphilis. I remember him explaining to the houseman that it was simply not possible as he had never slept with any other woman but his wife. How could he have syphilis if he had always been loyal to her? The houseman did not say anything. He just stood beside the bed, one hand on the head rail and the other on the bedspread, leaning forward a little and looking straight down at the patient with the truth written in his eyes. The patient suddenly collapsed into a torrent of sobs as that truth dawned on him. To see a man's spirit so mortally wounded was the most humbling experience I had.

There are plenty of other fragments of personalities that come back to me from those days in Arthur, and I feel frustrated that I am unable to complete them and give them a name. My links with the past are so often an unsatisfying chain of inconsequence that my memory has selected to store. Crises, of course, spin round like great ghosts, to bring back the individuals who were central to them. Sometimes patients created passages of memory that are unbroken and sharp because they touched some nerve that chose to hold them. But scores did not and I feel I am missing much that should still be there.

Arthur, however, did leave me with a larger legacy of patient memories than any other ward. I also had a good chance to get to know them well because of my more senior position. Responsibility suited me much better than sheer tempo. Once I had entered the realms of being in charge of a ward I was in my element. Those months on Arthur were the happiest of my training. Of course it must have helped that I was in love but it wasn't as simple as that. Arthur created the perfect environment for someone of my temperament, and that could be why it happened.

16

That October came our final exams. I had not looked forward to them with any particular dread but when they arrived that was another matter.

We were prepared for these, apart from our experiences on the wards, by our annual lecture periods at Riddell House, just across the road from St Thomas's, where most of the sisters lived. There was a large lecture hall there with the appropriate number of desks. Our sister tutor, of whom I have already made mention—and who seemed to me to be of tremendous age although she was rather younger than I am now—was a very tall, large, bespectacled woman with an impressive personality, who had a way with Nightingales. Her owl-like eyes would grasp the assembly, forcing concentration into even the most wavering minds. Even her back view demanded respect, as she wielded the chalk on the blackboard with fingers that looked as though they were red with chilblains even in summer.

I do not think I have ever met a personality that could be so ferocious with her subordinates, at times when she felt they deserved it. Yet was so universally loved by all who knew her. I remember her with the most deep and warm affection. She was one of three best teachers I have ever known. Years later, quite by chance, I found myself in a railway carriage with her on the way to Winchester. We discussed general matters that were not connected with the hospital and I found her as wise and as impressive as ever.

In spite of all this, we Nightingales did not always behave with the decorum expected of nurses during a very important part of their training, when we were in that lecture hall. Perhaps the main cause of our gaiety and indiscretions was the fact that, as a set, we were all together again, gathered up from the various wards, departments and outposts. Weeks and months could go by when we saw little of one another except, of course, individuals. But never as a group, because there were so many divisions—with day and night duty, outpatients, Hydestyle, the Grosvenor and Waterloo Hospitals. It was the immense spread of the hospital and its responsibilities, to say nothing of the many different nurses homes, that divided us. So those months on 'block', as they were called, were like big reunions.

I have kept, along with other venerable relics of those now distant days, a few jottings passed surreptitiously round our desks that had us bent double with laughter at the time. Of course, they were just parodies of what we were taught or what was said to us, the burlesque of the classroom being exaggerated mimicry.

'Nurses,' quoth one exuberant Nightingale, 'you must take copious fluids prophylactically before your viva voce on Thursday because in the circumstaaaaaaaaaaaances you will lose a lot of fluid by invisible excretion.'

Another Nightingale had written her contribution underneath: 'Drugs that affect the nervous system are drugs that affect the nervous system, examples are...(sneeze and blow of nose)...these are drugs that directly affect the nervous system.'

More scribblings underneath: 'In nephrosissss the blood pressure stays down, in nephritissssss it goes up (small torpedo of saliva with each S).'

And so forth. The final scribe's masterpiece at the bottom of the page is too crumpled to decipher and probably would not be repeatable if it was. Nightingales, like any other pupils could be irreverent at times.

There were several sister tutors who had to cope with teaching us. Now, thinking back, I had the greatest respect for all of them and learnt much from each. At the time, though, I can remember that sometimes we would ask them impossible questions, such that even our senior consultants might have had difficulty answering, and which information, perhaps, only a specialist of the highest order would ever have need of. We would wait in a hushed hall for the reply, and eventually were told to look it up for the next day. Asking questions of peculiar complexity, I did not just see as a form of tutor baiting. Even at school I can remember pupils asking questions so intricate that it seemed to expose more about the character of the person asking the question than anything else.

In spite of our weaknesses, the periods on 'block' were always a great success. Once the routine was established and we had settled down, learning began in earnest. Sister Tutor had a clever way of teaching with anecdote and emphasis, so that much of it became indelible. Her voice had exactly the right pitch and seemed to be made of several different threads, as she recounted stories of individual experience, of nursing events in other counties, and colouring what she said with her own brand of humour. She liked to make us laugh and had an amusing chortle herself which, in itself, was infectious.

Then she had direct ways of banging in information with a hammer. This was another feature unmistakable about her way of teaching. On the subject of the transmission of germs, for instance—a matter that dominated so much of what we were taught—she would give graphic descriptions of why sepsis was so prevalent after battles. 'Wounds', she said, 'were all washed from the same bucket with the same water.'

I can clearly remember the shock and alarm this information caused me. I thought of the dying Andre after the battle of Borodino in *War and Peace*—a book that had particularly moved and influenced my early adulthood—and all his sufferings due to wound sepsis. I also wondered if Tolstoy had not had such an easy way of letting him die, whether he might have been allowed to live and marry Natasha. Or would that have ruined the story?

The development and transmission of germs was anyway an aspect of medicine that held me captive. Because I could not understand why it had taken mankind so long to grasp this seemingly obvious (for those who know about it) matter. The fact that germs could not be seen seemed a poor excuse. Much odder facts than that had been discovered. And, anyway, the results of what germs did were so visible.

Nor was I convinced by the second excuse that they had remained a mystery. That they multiplied by spontaneous generation. One did not have to be a Pasteur to realise that not every living creature multiplied by the sexual factor. Who, for instance, as a child had not cut a worm in two and got two worms?

So, in spite of all Sister Tutor's patient teaching on the matter, I never came any nearer to understanding why mankind had taken so long to come to grips with microbes. Even if the reasons for the pathological changes in a wound were not comprehended, why hadn't the best ways to treat them been learnt? I suppose if one works in a major teaching hospital, with all the facts laid before one—which affect most of one's work—it is hard to believe that only a few decades have passed since the part germs played was beginning to be properly understood.

Sister Tutor called the white blood corpuscles, 'the body's troops' and pus, 'the carnage after the battle'. I remember so well on one occasion in Christian when a woman had had two pints of pus drained from her thigh. The skin had been tight and shiny white as though it had been polished or varnished and was exceedingly tender to touch. So it had been lanced and out had poured a torrent of pus like some terrible underground pollution. I questioned Sister Tutor about the speed with which the body could replace so many dead blood corpuscles. It seemed the body is astonishingly well equipped to replace its troops almost instantaneously.

She also taught us much about the various levels of pain and which pains were the worst and why. She said the most acute pains were caused by unnatural pressure from within one of the body's organs. I think she was particularly referring to kidney and gallstones, although I came across similar types of pain that were equally atrocious. One of these was from retention of urine in the bladder.

One old man was unable to relieve himself following an operation, apparently been made worse by all the normal tap running methods we had used to try and help him. While still waiting for the doctor to come and pass a catheter, he worked himself up into such a gasping panic, his face puffed in a purple frenzy of pain, that I wondered if he might not die from exhaustion before the doctor came. The whole affair blew up so quickly, and there must have been ten minutes of screaming before the relief of the catheter.

The subject for which our set will remember Sister Tutor the best—and which she repeated on numerous occasions so that it became the idée fixe of the classroom—was prophylaxis. Prophylaxis was the fountain of her teaching and whenever I hear that word I think of her.

The consultants took a large part in teaching us as well. A different surgeon, physician and gynaecologist was allocated to each set and eventually signed their certificates. It was our gynaecologist who was the most stimulating.

I have always liked gynaecologists. They are a special breed—an intimate breed, a witty breed—who, in my experience, get closer mentally and spiritually to their patients than other consultants. Our gynaecologist was from the cream of gynaecologists. He sent tremors of wakefulness through the lecture hall—every ear grew rigid with concentration as be divulged his 'tales from the gynae woods'.

First, there was the matter of conception. Babies could be conceived at any time of the menstrual cycle—there was no such thing as the safe period, not even during the 'curse'. That was a stunning start. He then went on to tell us that even those who were virgo intacta could conceive and not by immaculate conception either. It was all so different from conventional methods and timing—the temperature charts, the single ovulation and the ovum that had to be caught on the dot. Ova did appear to have a short life. It was the sperm who were the culprits. Often living for three weeks or more, lurking around waiting for an ovum to fertilize. No contraceptive were foolproof and the only way to be sure of not conceiving was abstention in, if possible, separate beds.

By this time most of the Nightingales were numb with concentration. Then he went on with tales of ovarian cysts the size of footballs or bigger. Women would come in with abdomens like beer barrels, that were only cysts that had got out of hand. Another cause for abdominal enlargement was phantom pregnancies. There was one where the woman had convinced him that there was a foetal heartbeat, but there was nothing inside. Even stranger, I found, were the babies born to women who did not realise that they were pregnant and thought that their active, kicking babies were just 'wind', and their vanished waistlines, the middle-aged spread. In fact, women having babies without foreknowledge of their pending arrival seemed more common than I would have believed possible.

He recounted one story of a young woman who had woken up one morning feeling that she must go quickly to the lavatory and instead of what was expected, she passed a baby. Worse than that, there was another woman who had given birth to a baby without realising she had done so. What? Yes, she had come in for examination with abdominal pains and it was found that her uterus hadn't properly contracted after having given birth. Where was the baby? She denied that she had had one and didn't know anything about it. She was perfectly compos mentis, was not drugged, had not been in a coma, was not drunk or anything else. She just did not know she had had a baby, albeit a premature one. So where was the baby? I cannot remember the end of that story but think it was another one that went down a drain—this time the whole way.

Then there was the strange but elaborately christened hydatidiform mole—and all those babies conceived at different times but gestated at the same one. Equally fascinating were the various different places in the body that babies have tried to grow. Not with any success, but there was always the occasional one that, if it did not make the grade, came closer to it than was historically possible. The ectopic pregnancy was a sizable hazard. Nothing that the imagination could reach seemed to be outside the range of the reproductive system. There was never a second of boredom during those lectures. I would not have minded them double the length.

The physician who lectured us also had a few unusual theories and sent at least one sacred cow of the nursing world off to the abattoir. That was on the question of 'bowel movement'. Now, it must be difficult for those who have not worked in a hospital, to realise how this specific action seems to involve everyone as though the progress of each patient depended on its regularity. As probationers, we had gone smartly round the ward twice a day, checking on the patients and reporting any lacunae. So that dosage could be administered that night in order that regularity could be restored the next day. It was automatic nursing policy and, if I were ever asked to put the nursing profession under various headings, the bowels would come at the top of one of them.

However, during our lectures, the physician seemed to suggest that the daily habit in this matter was less important than we had been led to believe. He recounted one story of a man who had not 'been' for some weeks, but was still leading a normal life. In other words, he was not ill. Obviously this was not a particularly desirable state of affairs but, what he was trying to indicate by this extreme example, was that man's health depended on it less than tradition had persuaded him that it did.

This was a minor thunderbolt to us Nightingales. Not just because we were nurses. But because our whole upbringing had made its daily occurrence a modus operandi. How much woolly Milk of Magnesia had I swallowed down as a child to prove that? And wasn't the end of breakfast always accompanied by a signal from my mother or my nanny that playtime or school was still one significant event away?

Another sacred nursing cow that came into some question during that time was sleep. That patients should sleep well was generally considered essential. To achieve it, nearly every patient was given the appropriate barbiturate nightly. Very few patients refused them and most were encouraged to accept them, in spite of the hangovers these drugs frequently gave. As a night nurse one would have felt a failure, with a ward full of wakeful patients. With one or two, I remember being allowed to repeat the dosage in the middle of the night if the patient woke up. Patients *had* to sleep and, in spite of the images so often portrayed of noisy, groaning wards in hospitals by those who imitate them, most people did. I can remember long nights on duty when hardly a murmur of sound broke the gentle harmony of human breathing.

This, ideally, was what one tried to achieve. That they slept was part of the seal of one's nursing abilities. One could not conceive of having to give a report in the morning, admitting to a ward full of wakeful patients. Nevertheless, I can remember our physician telling us that it was rest that was the vital requisite for recovery. And that not all individuals needed long periods of sleep to achieve it. Certainly, in the private wing of the hospital, I can remember the occasional patient reading the small hours away. But there was always an undercurrent of anxiety about it—as though it wasn't *right*. In the main wards such a policy would not have been practical. So the soneryls, sodium amytals and evipans were handed out nightly. Although for some people the side effects were a punishment in themselves.

During our lectures, our ears would pick up information on the seamier side of ill health. Those illnesses that through their habits and weaknesses, patients had brought upon themselves. People have always been inclined to ruin their health with alcohol, tobacco and drugs, and everyone knew it. But it is difficult now with Aids striking at the mighty, as well as many others, to think back to the time when venereal diseases were kept out of sight. Our training came at a time when antibiotics had come to grips with all venereal diseases so, for recent sufferers, there was a quickly redeemable situation.

However, for those older patients who had suffered from syphilis, it still presented a problem. It had seemingly remote signs and symptoms that came back to bother patients at different stages of their lives. One of these was an extremely serious condition (loyalty would still prevent me naming it) that could cause rapid death when the sufferer was of a more advanced age. Though this illness could be caused by other factors, we were led to believe that it was generally the result of a syphilitic infection in its terminal stages.

So when I used to see this given as cause of death in the obituary columns of some outstanding hero or exemplary citizen, I would find myself reassessing the life that seemed so weathered in good conduct, and find it more interesting for that. Nowadays, when it is commonplace to blow the gaffe about even our greatest men and women, it would be of little interest. But, in those days, characters could be made to seem unimpeachable and a thimbleful of human failing did their image no harm to us nursing students.

Our lectures in surgery were given to us by Mr Nevin, the third signature that adorns my Nightingale Certificate. Mr Nevin was one of those omnipotent beings on the wards who, at lecture times, became approachable and witty and seemed to enjoy teaching us. Perhaps it was a welcome change from the chaps. He, like the others, stimulated our minds to consider different angles of well worn themes but I suppose it was when they crossed the paths of nursing dogma, or illuminated the areas of once dark but fascinated ignorance, that we tended to remember most clearly what they said.

The exams came in October. We took our St Thomas's exams on the spot but were sent to other venues for the practical State exams. I was sent to a small hospital in south-east London where some un-frightening examiners nodded their heads at my fracture bed and my setting for lumber puncture. And asked me some straight forward questions about them and other matters. Some of the equipment seemed rather odd and different from ours. Otherwise nothing happened to alarm me.

We had to wait till November for our results and, I believe, all but one of our set passed. The pass rate was usually high. After all the endeavours of those who taught us, it should have been. It was good, though, to have it over.

17

After we had passed our final exams and moved into our fourth year, our uniform dresses changed from purple and white stripes to pale blue and white, but otherwise remained the same. That fourth year, which we understood was supposed to repay the hospital for our training in the previous three, was also necessary to receive the Nightingale Certificate and badge. Most nurses stayed that extra year—we would not have felt complete without it.

Unfortunately, it did not start very well for me because I was sent to work in the theatre. In those days there were three theatres, all of them in some inner sanctum of the hospital, where hardly a shaft of light managed to penetrate their well-like interiors or brighten their cabbage green walls. So perhaps it was the rather claustrophobic effect that this had, made me dislike the one I was sent to straight away.

But there was another indefinable factor. There seemed to be special unwritten codes in the theatres that everyone around me seemed to understand automatically, but which my floundering self never came to grips with. Because there were no patients around, except unconscious ones, to soften the atmosphere; and because the homogenization of the garments we were compelled to wear made many people, even if one knew them, difficult to recognize; and because the organization of our duties was done singly, even though each was linked intangibly together, I felt a remoteness I never managed to penetrate, hard as I sometimes tried. To me the theatre was a combination of blade-bone reactions, and impersonal service, to an accompaniment of an assortment of noises, most noticeably the cathedral organ pump of anaesthesia.

I was later to learn that my first impressions of the theatre held nothing so macabre as those of my friend Jo. On the very first day that she stepped into its arena, she was handed a severed leg for disposal which, she reported, finished her.

Orthopaedic operations, for the novice, were pretty hair-raising I found. Although I adjusted easily—and with interest—to the abdominal and thoracic operations, I was made queasy, to the point of shock, by all the sawings, the wrenchings, the twistings, that went on with bones and joints. This was not helped by the fact that, as tourniquets had to be applied for certain parts of the operations to prevent a blood bath, the limbs appeared as white as alabaster and were almost wax-like in appearance and texture. To see a ball end of a bone shine through a glistening, bloodless ligament made me feel very sick. I just could not look. But although I could turn my head away, I could not block up my ears. And the crunchings and grindings played the same nasty tricks with my imagination, as had done the sight of all the carpentry and manipulations.

I was simply not a natural for this kind of scene. Yet, years later, I managed to get the courage to go and see our orthopaedic surgeon, Mr Furlong, with a foot complaint, and was prepared to lay myself down on the operating table at his mercy. Thankfully, after examining my foot, he gave it a nice little stroke, and said he thought I would be better to stay with medical treatment. Operations with my condition often led to more operations. I thanked him and was profoundly relieved.

In my earliest days in the theatre, I had some contact with patients when they arrived still awake, still people, still themselves—or almost themselves—in the little antechamber where they received their pentathol. I was often given the job of standing with them, trying to talk such an important part of their lives into irrelevance by conversational chicanery. I found that I was quite good at this and looked on it as a vital little stepping stone to perfect, before the anaeasthetist waded in, in his white Wellington boots and his syringe ready for action.

Once on the operating table and the scalpel was poised, I forgot the person I had been talking to as quickly as possible—the face, the voice, the feelings, the expressions, all became a blank. That was generally the last I saw of them. For, in those days, having no recovery room, they returned, tubes in mouths, to the wards, long before they returned to consciousness.

Eventually, after weeks of cleaning, of setting of trolleys, of shaking out bloodstained swabs on the floor for counting, and of dancing around behind the surgeons doing up their tapes, I was considered senior and competent enough to assist at minor operations. These events I dreaded in advance, as much as I had dreaded playing the piano at school concerts. From the beginning, as I stood behind the trolley, I found that I had ten rubber thumbs on my hands, reaching for the instruments and that threading catgut in a hurry, could be as difficult as putting a snake through the eye of a dog. The catgut dived around the eye of the needle but, on many occasions, simply refused to go through it. It was then that I witnessed—the only time in my presence—a surgeon allow himself the luxury of a little temper.

In all I was to assist at six operations. All of them trivial in real terms of strain. But each of which tattooed me with memories of ham-handedness. For the first two, at least, I had a senior Nightingale of the theatre staff to prompt me to reach for the cautery, the clamp, the suture—or whatever the surgeon needed—when sheer nervousness froze me, and my hands seemed incapable of following what my ears must have heard but, after a few supervisions, I was on my own. I quickly realised that, so accustomed were the surgeons to the sensitive and intuitive brilliance of the Nightingale sisters and charge nurses—who no doubt anticipated their needs before they became apparent to the surgeons themselves—that my inexperience and ineptitude stuck out like an illuminated obelisk.

On one particular occasion, when the surgeon simply put out his hand expecting me to know with what to fill it, I found myself so overcome by a confusion of instincts ingrained from a well trained and mannered childhood, that it very nearly made me take his hand and grasp it—before a growl informed me that it was scissors that he required. All the confidence that had been built up in three ward years vanished like so many shaggy ghosts during those weeks. Never was a woman less suited to a role than I to that one.

One of the kings of our theatre stage was Mr Boggon, a surgeon and a name synonymous with our life and times. He looked like a Roman nobleman with a suitable nose, well furnished about the face, small eyes and a broad back. And he was as hard a task master as any Roman, I am sure. Had I ever been in a position of handing him instruments, fear would have petrified me. Luckily such people only had the best in the way of attendants. The scullions, like myself, kept out of the way as much as possible. Nevertheless, it was still possible to listen to what he said and observe his skills, and his little shafts of humour when his eyes danced above his mask. When I first saw him operate I noticed that his hands appeared to shake a little and wondered how he could perform so effectively with such a handicap. It appeared that was how he always was and it made no difference. Mr Boggon died only quite recently and I was very sad to read about it. He was a man with such presence, and one who was so much here on earth.

I cannot remember that there were any brain operations in the theatre that I worked in. The most serious operation that I witnessed was on the heart, called a mitral valvulotomy and, although I saw a number of these operations, I never heard of anyone die as a result. There was, however, one amusing incident I saw connected with it.

Inevitably it first required the removal of several ribs with a large, ominous looking instrument. As this instrument was performing its duty, one of the ribs flew into the air. With astonishing force it hit the glass perimeter of the balcony, where a bevy of watching medical students were clustered like starlings. They scattered in alarm and I have to admit that the sheer velocity of that airborne rib and the resounding lash of its force on the glass would have frightened me. The surgeon, however, thought it was a top class joke and let out a huge belly surge of laughter, infecting the whole theatre with ripples of amusement.

I suppose there must have been other moments such as that, that I have forgotten about. But try as I might, I cannot remember any diversional chat about kippers, or other humdrum conversational distractions, that surgeons are supposed to talk about. If there were jokes they seemed to be on the job. I expect there must have been periods in the theatre when I thought it was fun. But, when my time was up, I returned to the wards with a heart that had been put back in its proper place.

Apart from my difficulties in the theatre at that time, I had been moved to Gassiot House, the nurses' home adjoining the hospital. I think I was one of the few nurses to develop an aversion to this place, but dislike it I did. I was in a room on the top floor, right at the end of the corridor which had a cell-like bleakness with its flecked stone floors and mole coloured walls. Also I was plagued by sleeplessness, mostly because Big Ben not only stared directly into my room, but at times seemed to get into bed with me.

During those sleepless nights, I would try to get responses from my tub like wireless—or wrote streams of poetry about love, or anything that could fill up the time. There was one about Michelangelo's great sculpture of Moses, which took up pages of an exercise book before I dropped off to sleep. The only pleasure I found in Gassiot House was playing the piano in the sitting room. Once, when immersed in 'The Revolutionary Study'—the only piece I knew off by heart—a nurse appeared from St Thomas's Home, the private wing underneath, to inform me politely that I was disturbing the afternoon slumbers of the patients. So my piano playing came to an end. In addition to all this, my affair with Peter had recently ended and I was as low as I have been in my life.

Early in 1955, though, my life came right again. After a special request I was sent back to Cheyne House and was removed from the theatre to work at St Thomas's Home. Here I stayed for the remainder of my training with a brief interlude of a few weeks in City once more. It was the Home that dominated my last year and in every way I was supremely happy there. There seemed to be so little pressure and it was so quiet in comparison with the big wards, with its little pockets of mostly single units. For part of the time I worked upstairs with the women and for the other, downstairs with the men.

I made two particular friends with the men. One was a colonel who had come in to have an operation for cancer of the colon. Immaculately a gentleman, even when semiconscious after his operation, his politeness was like liquid gold. When there was time, I would often try to help him with his *Times* crossword, as I had done with that colonel in George Makins. In another, but equally strong way, the bonds between us developed.

He was probably the most totally charming and exquisitely mannered patient I ever nursed. He wrote to me after his discharge, thanking me for all I had done—which really had not amounted to the sum of his gratitude. I was very shaken to hear, only three months later, that he had died. Had I not already decided to give up nursing once my training was finished, his death would have made me certain. I had reached the stage when the death of patients who had become so dear, was a regular feature of a nurses life that I could not face up to.

The other patient to claim my affection was a certain Dr Frank Schofield. He was Canadian and referred to himself as a displaced person from Canada. He came into the Home for an operation to try to salvage the remains of his dwindling sight. He was a deeply religious man and had a towering personality that he hid under a rather arcadian veneer. He did not treat any of the nurses as nurses. He treated them as friends. One of the nurses he called 'my good nurse, Miss Banbury'. I was referred to as his 'dear child'. He never became familiar with us, through first names or cheek. He just cared about us, as though we were his family. This included talking to us as long as we could possibly afford. He talked in philosophical sweeps, in poetry, in the language of lovers, and wrote down his favourite poems that were his recipe for living and gave them to the nurses. I still have mine.

Before he came into hospital he had been working for the rehabilitation of war refugees in Munich. He was to return there after his discharge, where he was to start a society for Yugoslav refugees in particular. But his eyesight broke down again and he was admitted to an eye hospital in Basle. From there he wrote me one of the longest and profoundest letters I have ever received.

I will never forget the day he was discharged. We had a tender, almost tearful farewell. He had given a cake to the nurses as a parting present. But I was feeling so upset I could not eat my share. When I returned on duty I found he had left a little note for me.

To Night Supervisor Coventry—A Last Sad Lament

How dare my thoughtless little nurse,
Despise the cake I did disperse
And hope to keep affection still,
Impossible! And yet she will.

I like to think that Frank had a considerable effect on my life. He taught me that good feelings are better expressed; affection shown. That nothing is too ordinary to investigate or have interest in, and that almost all problems, disappointments and difficulties can be turned to some good, and be used. He was a delicious optimist, revelling in possibilities. Even when his eyesight had almost gone, he believed that God would provide, by recharging and revitalizing his other senses. He wrote to me:

> I have to pray very often but I believe that all things work together for good to those who love God. Life is full of interest—you are a dear child. Affectionately Frank.

It was perhaps appropriate that my time at St Thomas's should end with him. Two weeks later I gave a small farewell party on the ward the night before I left. But it was a flat affair. I felt exactly the same as the man who had spoken those immortal lines from 'Salad Days':

> It's not that I want to stay, it's just that I don't want to go.

18

When I started nursing, and when I ended it too, the pay was very little. Yet, in all the years, I do not remember one Nightingale abandoning her training because of this. It was officially stated that we received £ 200 a year before tax with deductions for our keep (lumped together under the word 'emoluments') of approximately £100. So we were left with a salary of about £7 a month (this doubled when we were S.R.N.s). My first cheque, I can clearly remember, was £6-14-0d. It seemed to vary, for my third cheque was £5-8-0d and my fourth was £8 dead.

This variation in the amount of money we received was a mystery which I did not bother to solve. But it had nothing to do with the hours worked. Our hours of work were supposed to be sixty a week. One week I can remember nearly ninety hours worked (that must have been exceptional or I would have forgotten about it). This did not augment my salary or alter anything except the time I was free. At the end of every month we queued up to receive our money, which was delivered to us ceremoniously in the main hall under the stairs, on an enormous cheque. I remember how excited we were, almost as if it were something that we had not earned.

Nobody in those days considered that we were paid too little—rather the reverse. We were often told (and I do not mean by the hospital staff) how lucky we were to get our training free and to be paid into the bargain. Not long before, nurses had had to pay to be trained. Now they were receiving money instead. What luxury it seemed in comparison. I think that was how we must have considered it ourselves for—although I don't suppose there were many amongst our rather undemanding generation who really felt they had enough money (what young person does)—we did not make an issue of it. It was just a fact of life.

Shortage of money may not have driven many Nightingales out of the hospital. But sometimes other factors did. Out of the fifty of us who entered the Nightingale Training School together in my set, forty six completed the training. Of the four who fell by the wayside, one left to get married and another for medical reasons. The remaining two were considerably older than the majority of us, and they may have found the training a little sharp for their maturer years. Had I been their age, I might not have survived the training either. But, at nineteen, it seemed like a continuation of a routine and disciplined life up to that stage.

I was in no position to judge that then. When I was nineteen I did not know how people change in their twenties. How that brief, flying decade (as it seems now) wipes clean the childhood slate, and mentally puts one in quite a different gear. At nineteen, in those days, most girls of the type that became nurses had only known their homes and the disciplines of their respective schools. What had happened to us outside had always been under long or short distance supervision. I had known certain freedoms. I was very lucky in this respect. But those freedoms always came within the immense influence that my parents had on the way I felt and acted. I believe my mother chose all my clothes till I left school and went on persuading me for years afterwards that permanent waves were the answer to fine and unruly hair. Although I detested them myself, I went on having them done—and my friends were similarly influenced by their parents. We must have been quite a compliant generation and, as such, were perfect material for a training as fluent as the Nightingale one.

Once there, we found that we were all in the same boat. Our lives were bound by exactly the same opportunities and limitations. The sisters would not have been human if they had not preferred certain characters amongst the students they taught. But this would never have budged them one inch when it came to measuring up to the standards required. No one had privileges or rights during their training that everyone else did not have. I can think of no other existence where luck played such a minuscule role as it did in that one.

The only selection came at the end of our training, when those nurses who had accumulated the highest examination marks and the best reports on nursing skills and conduct, were awarded medals. There were three of these: gold, silver and bronze. The nurses who won them were also awarded an Honours Certificate. We all had a fair chance to gain these accolades. The Nightingale training was essentially a fair one, so that many of the human stresses that exist in other careers, did not touch us.

Only occasionally (like during my first night duty) did I think the training was tough. I took for granted that the type of training that we received was normal in all hospitals at the time. It is only now, when I get together with my old Nightingale cronies, that we are convinced—even with all the additional skills that a modern day nurse might have to have—that our lives were harder. In the fifties we were not cushioned by all the technological innovations that divide and subdivide the length of the treatments. The huge cost of the N.H.S. now, was—anyway in part—the sweat on our brows then.

The complexity of much of what we did, the perpetual battle with sterilizing, the scrubbing, the cleaning and the demanding timescales, have been replaced by the packaged, the disposable, the unbreakable, longer periods of rest, and an army of ancillary workers that turns the wheels of most of a hospital's domestic chores. Those changes I would have welcomed. But I would not like to have been the tears of society's conscience. Or even a 'special case'. We were taught that to nurse sick people was a privilege. No one owed us a living. We were there to serve the ill and honoured to do so.

How easy, I used to think, it was to feel that. Take one example. Sometimes, after a fairly arduous period of duty, I would change out of my uniform and walk along the fringes of the Embankment, or through Parliament Square to St James's Park, and lean on the bridge watching the ducks land in graded perfection on the lake. Or I might go shopping in the Army and Navy where a scarf in a sale would send my spirits soaring. Then I would return to the wards in an afterglow of revitalized energy and pleasure at seeing the patients again. I was never sorry to go off duty, but I was always pleased to come back. More than anything else this proved to me how happy I was.

None of my pleasure in nursing was conditioned by the fact that I had known from the beginning that there was a limit on it. It was not a career in which I could happily have spent the rest of my life. I longed to do something in the arts, although at that stage I wasn't quite sure what. Yet, while it lasted, I always felt that it gave me more than it took away and whilst I had those feelings I would not have left it.

As far as pay was concerned, had I been given ten times what I was, it would have undoubtedly made me more adventurous. It would certainly have made me smarter (although I have to admit, that was the one period of my life when I was often flattered for my taste in clothes—in winter I always wore a hat, gloves, and carried a long, rolled umbrella). It would probably have given me more confidence, at a time of life when confidence is at a premium—and particularly our generation that did not have much of it anyway. But I am not certain if it would have made any difference to my decision to enter nursing. Or whether it would have kept me, or substantially improved my happiness or morale, whilst I was there.

Money was a curiously undominant feature of our lives in the fifties. Although the majority of my set had had comfortable backgrounds, we were as mentally detached from money as it would be possible to make young people of our age. This must have been partly due to our wartime childhoods, where rationing and scarcities had made any sort of material spoiling impossible. But also because money per se had a slightly suspicious smell about it amongst the sort of people who were nice to know.

It was much smarter in those days to be not too smart. The worn, the weathered, the mended, the dyed, the remodelled there was cleverness and satisfaction in all that. Guilt would place a clammy hand on my heart, when I spent money where it was frivolous, extravagant or unnecessary to do so. In my letters to my mother I would continually refer to the providence in my spending, giving the exact cost of a piece of clothing, an outing or a present. Often following it up with a comment about how cheap it really was. And making a comparison, if I felt it necessary with how much I could have spent had I been less careful.

In fact, the double experience of having had Victorian/Edwardian mothers, with the limitations and restrictions of a depression and a war during our formative years, imprisoned most of us in a cell of guilt about spending. Even now, most of my generation seems to want to explain away any suggestion of extravagance. 'A cashmere sweater?' Came from a jumble sale. 'A house in Tuscany?' Bought with a legacy, costs nothing to run. 'Computer for the ten year old son?' Bought at a knock down price. As though there is something fundamentally wrong about spending, and it can only he mentioned derogatorily. There seems a special language of its own to do with acquisitions, that is widely used amongst a certain type and age of Englishwoman understood totally within the group that uses it. But the seeds for which were planted so long ago, we have forgotten how they came.

When I used to write to my parents from St Thomas's saying that I was broke, it was sometimes a matter of pride and not a begging bowl for more. Caution with money was ingrained in my soul, but clichés like 'making ends meet' that fell from the lips of so many enquirers, I found boring. With all our creature comforts catered for and our needs so stunted by lack of opportunity, we managed. I was lucky, too, because I had a small additional allowance from my parents. So managing on a very limited income was not the impossible task it might seem today.

We were just coming into the New Look then. Yet, with all the extra material required, coats cost only about £7. I bought a tweed coat for that price that was so beautifully made, it would have lasted me a lifetime. And shoes, leather throughout, only cost about£3—and most of the other clothes I bought were equally cheap and durable. Also they had hems, they had good seams—they could be let down and in and out at will. They were made from natural materials, so they could be dyed.

The rest of my possessions had the same qualities. My Parker fountain pen (the one I dropped into the bed pan) of which I was very proud and still use, I had had since I was thirteen. My wireless, definitely low fidelity, was stout and durable and never needed repairing. My alarm clock survived until recently. It expired finally, after having been dropped down a flight of stairs. All my possessions had a touch of permanency about them and I treated them as though they might not be able to be replaced.

Apart from all this, there was a very low cut-off in my level of expectations in general. Until the war, I had spent most of my early life abroad in various ports with my naval father. But in England, holidays had just been spent with relations. So the simple holidays I managed to go on with other Nightingales—to the Channel Islands or the north of France—seemed like luxury. And were, as measured by our standards then. All travel seemed relatively much cheaper than it is now. As far as concerts and theatres were concerned, we were often offered free seats for those.

Perhaps our greatest expense was our black nylon stockings. They cost 5/- a pair. Although they did not ladder quite so easily as tights do now, I remember that there was a great deal of cobbling of ladders to make them last longer. But, in general, our expenses were low and prices were almost static. If anyone had mentioned the word inflation to me, I would not have known what was meant. Or what it does to people in the way of greed and unscrupulousness. No, in retrospect, I think we could count many blessings that, at the time, we did not even know we had.

19

And that, in normal circumstances, would have been nearly the end of my story. But it did not work out like that. Soon after I had started to write this book, I was taken very seriously ill. That experience, in some ways so different from what I might have imagined, not only taught me in detail what I could not have learnt any other way. But also the truth in all the finer points of our training. For that reason, and for a comment made by a night nurse about Nightingales, I thought it worth recording.

People who have been nurses proverbially know both too much and too little when illness comes into their own homes. About my children's health, I was continually worried in their younger days, giving every symptom that occurred its most sinister reason. Every time there was a wheeze or an unaccountable pain, two and two made six. Of all the various stresses of child-rearing, my children's illnesses were the events I dreaded the most and found I was least rational about. Never was the tiniest doubt allowed to go uninvestigated.

But to my own health, I had had reason to give very little thought. Apart from various complications to do with my pregnancies, I had never been into hospital as an adult. I seemed to suffer almost no trivial illnesses and even the allergies of my younger days had reached the stage where no specific remedy was necessary. I had a dislike of needlessly worrying doctors. Except for sleeping pills, I rarely visited one and never called one out.

Therefore, when I woke up in the middle of a spring night a few years ago with sharp pains in my chest and shoulder, I did not fear the worst—as I would have done with my children. I treated it lightly. I had had a drenching in the rain a few days earlier and rheumatism was a family complaint. It was, I decided, a nasty attack of that.

I got up the next morning to take my son back to school. By the evening, I felt quite ill and had a temperature, so put myself to bed.

The following day I was no better, but still hesitated to call a doctor. On the third day, however, I rang the surgery and a doctor came and diagnosed pneumonia. I was astonished at this. It had never crossed my mind that a person who had had no cold or other prior infection could get pneumonia—with no suspicion of a forewarning, or any history of chest infection, up to that time. Nevertheless, that was what seemed to have happened. So I swallowed down the penicillin capsules that were prescribed. Improvement did occur. I was recommended to go out into the beautiful sunshine in the garden, which I did. But suddenly my condition rapidly worsened. One night, ten days after I had first become ill and, following a visit from another doctor who had found nothing to alarm him, I told my husband that I thought I was dying.

There is a stage in this strange process of worsening illness when the mind moves substantially away from interest in all that is around you, into that little central well that is yourself. Inside that well, you are no longer rational, you have no experience, you are cut off from life's processes and the senses diminish slowly and surely, until they stop giving their messages. Had this not happened to me so effectively, I would surely have had my worried husband by-pass the doctor signal and call an ambulance. But I still wanted to believe what I was told—that I was on the mend. Also, encapsulated in my tiny world, I did not want to give up the fight on my own—although I had not become so remote from reality to realise my chances of winning were now becoming slim.

Two days later, two days weaker, the doctor who had first visited me again calmly administered her reassurance. My temperature was down, my blood pressure up a little. But she was pleased about that—in two days time I would be well, she was certain. Half an hour after her visit, my left leg went into a massive thrombosis. The sharp pain stirred me out of my semi-conscious state. I watched with fear and fascination the leg take on a mottled, purple appearance and swell up like a tyre before my eyes. Now, at last, the solid evidence of what must have seemed like the vagaries of my imagination, was there for all to see. An ambulance was called.

The ambulance men were angels: I shall remember them all my

life. Lifting me up and wrapping me in blankets like the most fragile china, they carried me downstairs. I was then borne along to the Charing Cross Hospital.

'You will be walking out of here,' one of them said to me.

I blessed him for saying it but I did not believe it could be true. My former memories of such conditions had flown, leaving me groping, as a layman gropes, with likely speculation.

In the casualty department, staff blew in and out. A beaming woman student asked me questions. Another looked down at me like a god and I told him what a lovely face he had. A nurse wiped the sweat from round my neck and another gave me an injection of pethidine. It did not work—my circulation was not strong enough. Interested students surrounded my bed—and one of them went off to search for a camera. My leg was a fairly rare sight. All the while I was waiting, with an increasing sense of urgency, for someone to trust. For in that twilight world there was nothing else to latch onto.

That someone came in the nature of a registrar. His appearance was the anchor onto which I attached my floating awareness. In his delicate touch I read my recovery. With lightning speed he assimilated the minutiae of my case. Questions, answers, conclusions—questions, answers, conclusions. After quite a short time he made his decisions. So much did the concern, insight and wisdom of that man impress my feeble self that my morale suddenly lifted and I felt much better. So, when I was told I was going to be sent to Intensive Care, I was surprised.

Within half an hour I was being artificially fed into my veins with dextroxe, saline and proteins. Anticoagulants joined the mêlée of tubes from the then, quite new to me, sage pump. Oxygen was in my nostrils and my chest was attached to an electrocardiograph and I watched my heart rollick around like a giddy little clown. Shortly afterwards, a mobile X-ray machine appeared and immediately identified the real source of my acute illness—a large blood clot in my right lung. Then I was taken with all my numerous attachments down to X-ray for a venogram which showed that every major vein in my leg was blocked. This apparently terrible news caused everyone, including myself, relief. At least it was not an artery.

The personnel who looked after me achieved all this with the artistry of genius. For in that hour of intense activity to save my life, I noticed not the slightest degree of haste and I felt no pain. The nurses and doctors who attended me moved around my gilded cage like people in some mystical ballet. Performing automatic roles, supporting one another, having everything that was needed to hand. I watched them through quickening consciousness and sharpening senses, totally absorbed by their excellence and bewitching kindness.

I went back there, weeks later, to tell them how profound was my gratitude, but it was not possible to say it in words. They told me that the nurses who worked in Intensive Care were mostly chosen from outside the hospital so there was a selection from most of the major London teaching hospitals: St Bartholomews, Guy's, the Middlesex, the UCH and, I am happy to say, one very pretty Nightingale. In charge was a large Australian doctor who, still in the true power, health and glamour of burgeoning youth, told me, from the depths of his biblical beard and with eyes as tender as the night, that I had many, many years of life ahead of me yet. How was it possible, after that, not to recover?

In fact, so successful were they all in turning crisis into recovery that, after two days, I was moved down to 8th South. My first few days there were not pleasant ones and I will not elaborate all the many things that appeared to go wrong, through no fault of the devoted staff who looked after me. The outcome was that it was decided, owing to the fact that I needed so many treatments, to move me from the little ward for four that I was in, to one of my own. It was in that room, on the first day, that I turned the final corner towards recovery.

One of the factors, in turning the tide that played a part, was a performance that afternoon on the wireless of Verdi's 'Il Trovatore'. Devoted to classical music since my early twenties, I had had little opportunity to go to concerts or operas for months—and classical music was not the favourite choice for my trendy children. But I could now indulge myself. Pressing the various knobs on the adjustor, I came into the opera when Leonora was singing 'Tacea la notte placida'. The sounds moved inside me as though they were my blood. I had quite forgotten the immense power of music to stir vivid reactions in those who care for it. I was lifted and changed from a pit of apathy and limpness into someone who felt joined together again.

That evening, a nurse looked at me with widened eyes. 'You look so different. When I went off duty I thought to myself, I hope she's going to be all right.'

'I sang this afternoon,' I told her.

'Yes, someone told me they heard you singing.'

That was the real beginning—after that I knew I would get well.

The following day my registrar inspected my leg which had become so deflated he teasingly said, 'Remind me which is the bad one.' By this time, my legs looked almost identical in their white elasticated stockings. A few days before, when I was having a blood transfusion and the pneumonia had caught hold again to such an extent I could hear fluid at the bottom of my lungs, he had told me, 'we are not through the wood yet.' But that morning he gave me a look that told me we very nearly were.

I lay in my bed thinking. Of the sick state now, I was truly a connoisseur. I had been there—I knew. No longer was it something that I viewed from the outside, with the imperfect knowledge of those who imagine and feel, however profoundly, but cannot really construct from the bottom up. The acute weakness, the lassitude, the resignation—all surprised me. I found that I was uncharacteristically calm. So little mattered except trying to get comfortable. Time shifted around me in spasms. Sometimes caressing me into sleep. Other times forcing me into major activities, like pulling myself up the bed or talking to a visitor. All the while I remained detached. The life I lived had moved away from me and no longer belonged.

At the beginning I did not even reflect on the comparisons, so great were they. Then I realised that at home I was constantly at the centre of little silts of problems, intrusive elements, unprepared moments, and of the happiness that I made for myself, and was not dependant on others providing. Here, in hospital, I was just conscious of the ebb and flow of routine and the tiny part I played in it. A spectator, all the normal worries of my life had taken themselves away into their own secret hiding places.

My registrar said to me, 'We are here to do the worrying for you.'

Yes, yes—that was it. They were there to do the worrying. There was time to waste and it was limitless and much of it was my own. I could fritter it, indulge it, wallow in it, survey it from outside. Time—time—those blessed moments that slip away from the healthy but spread out before the sick in open abundance. While I was still ill enough, but not too ill, I found its gentle passing gave me the luxury of mental ease. These feelings were so positive they must have helped me to get well.

The hospital vicar came to talk to me about it. Did I feel that illness had changed me in any way? Yes, I thought it had but not in a way I could easily define. I had nearly died but it had not frightened me. The prospect of death in the pit of illness had seemed to me good not bad. It had been an option to life that had been milked of its vitality and interest and that option had been like a great arm that would catch me if I fell. In spite of the fact that in my real life I had everything to live for. I had known that death might not have been far away. But I had never felt so close to its border that I would slip over it. Simply that the border had become a smooth and not a harsh one.

That, I told the vicar, was how I had changed the most. I saw it in a clearcut way; it was the fruits of life, its joys, its love, its purpose, that made death seem such an outrage. Without them, if there were no death, the prospects for life would be infinitely worse. Those revelations have helped me many times since, including during and after the death of my mother.

As far as being nursed was concerned—how beautifully tended I was. Those nurses etched in the finest detail, every memory of my Nightingale years that had been good. I blessed them, as they did for me all those duties I longed to do for myself but could not. They answered, without being asked, the touch of communication with the real and purposeful. And they had that double gift of speed with tranquility. How precious that is to the sick. What was it Sister

Elizabeth had said about me? That I was still a little noisy? Now I had good reason to know exactly what she meant. I enjoyed chatting to them, and through them, peering into my then distant past. I was continually drawing on their freshness and good humour and watched with interest every treatment they did to me.

There seemed to be many changes from my nursing days. The nurses had their surnames emblazoned on their chests but were, nevertheless, called by their first names. No patient of mine would have dared call me Sue. Nurse Coventry I was, except for the occasional nickname. But even that did not seem as intimate as a discovery of my first name. I liked the change, although I understand that this social approximation in hospitals is not welcomed by all. In the fifties we had only called children by their first names and some of the chaps, particularly the policemen. But no woman over thirty that I can remember. Certainly no one of my age.

As for nursing routine, it seemed to have—for want of a better word—homogenized. Instead of dividing duties to each patient, they were done together. This would have been impossible in the vast wards at St Thomas's, but in the small patchwork wards of the Charing Cross, it seemed sensible. Certainly, from the patients' point of view it was pleasant. Sometimes it was not necessary to wake me up with a thermometer much before 7 a.m., depending on which way the rounds were being done. Sometimes I would lie in bed and think of all the work, as a night nurse, I had done by seven. I wondered how it was organized there now.

The different styles of the hospitals were apparent in many ways. One of the most obvious was in the ward sister. In the first few days in that ward I did not think there was a sister. No one appeared to look any different from anyone else. So I asked.

'Of course we have a sister. She is the one in the little blue cloak.'

I found it hard to believe. She must have been all of twenty five, with her soft brown eyes and thick hair coiled up at the back. She blended in with the other nurses and seemed almost indistinguishable from the staff nurses. I remembered our sisters with their pebble-dash perms and their comforting greyness under their pert caps. Their apparent above-average height or build, and their burning authority stamped on every corner of the ward. The contrast was quite remarkable. It wasn't just that I had got so much older. I could not conceive of anyone being a sister at such a tender age and without the bustling exigency of a giant. Maybe it had always been that way at the Charing Cross.

'Whatever has happened to the older nurses?' I asked.

No one knew. On my many follow up visits to the hospital, I have seen one or two sisters who look as though they might have reached forty. But the majority look like girls.

In our day, at St Thomas's, most of the cleaning was done by the probationers and there had never been more than one ward maid or orderly on the ward at a time. In the Charing Cross of the eighties, ward maids swarmed around in droves on their stout Latin or West Indian legs (not many Cockneys now), changing water, offering drinks, delivering and collecting meal trays, cleaning and tidying. They wise-cracked with the patients and scolded them for their untidiness. No one made me feel smaller than the Spanish maid who cleaned my room.

'Two days ago this room was great. To-day, mess, mess, everywhere. You put your mess in bag I put for you. You too many flowers—they dead—I throw them out.'

What authority! I didn't answer back. Not all the patients were so submissive though. An old Cockney called Doris refused the apple and custard that was banged down in front of her and insisted that she had ordered icecream.

'You have apple and custard—there ain' no icecream.'

'I'll bloody 'ave icecream or I won't 'ave nothing.' And icecream Doris had.

Then there were the porters—so different from those of my Lambeth days, uniformed, almost military types, the salt of the earth and often the wrong side of fifty. These were jazzy joking lads in their twenties and thirties, dressed in blue polyester shirts and grey drip-dry trousers, sweating a little from the heat and all the work. Fed to the teeth but observant and aware with sound medical heads on their shoulders. They were kept busy, too. There are so many tests people have nowadays. Nearly every day the porters arrived to take me on a journey.

'Where are we going today,' I would ask.

'Scan,' they said and off my bed and I would go.

I was naturally fascinated by all the new tests. The scan, like beautiful paintings in sharp contrasts. And the amazing, mysterious ultrasound. Dr Ultrasound moved a mechanism that looked like a microphone over my abdomen. Up on the screen I was able to watch the revelations of what appeared like a seabed of floating objects, moving fins, black-eyed shapes, swaying this way and that in slow, caressing movements in their bodily tomb. Dr Ultrasound was quite satisfied.

'You are as fit as a fiddle,' he said with his nice, long face.

When it all came to an end and I was well enough to go on convalescence, I asked my registrar if he were pleased with the way things had gone.

'You have been a model patient,' he said.

But that was not really what I meant. I had wanted to know if I had recovered rather better and quicker than they had expected. Had my progress been surprisingly good and confounded some of the rather gloomy prognostications I had heard taught to the students by the consultant, just within my earshot? I think I had done that. Whether I had been a model patient in the real sense of the word, I rather doubt. At least, not as good as I would have liked to have been.

My first sin of commission came during those first nights in 8th South when it was discovered that a drug I was being given to make me sleep at night, was not written on my drug sheet. The nurse in charge came over and explained that I was only to be given a milder drug that night. If I wanted the other one it would mean recalling the houseman, who had already returned to his room for the night.

My mind flew back to Lambeth and those dedicated, tireless men and how, as a nurse, I had hesitated before calling them in the night. I imagined him, perhaps already in his pyjamas, settling down with a good book. Or even in bed with the lights out and the blackness licking round his disappearing consciousness.

Extremely ill as I was at that stage, I found it an easier battle to wrestle with my conscience than I had imagined as desperation gives one a fierce kind of selfishness but, in spite of my intense need, I was deeply sorry. He was fetched, however, and explained to me that I was in no fit state for my usual drug that night, which was why he had not made it available. I would have to manage with a milder one. I apologized for disturbing him unnecessarily and he departed.

The milder drug did not work, as I knew it wouldn't. Never having been in greater need of sleep than I was then, I committed the unforgivable sin. My husband had left my own sleeping pills in my wash bag close at hand. Although, certainly in Intensive Care, the nurses had known of the existence of these pills, they had not, for some reason, been taken away.

When the night nurse had gone, I levered myself onto my elbow and managed to find the energy to reach the jar and unscrew the top and retrieve a pill. No one knew. No one ever found out. My own reasoning, such as it existed, was that, had that additional pill caused me to die, it would have been better than struggling with an aching body all night. In fact, death at that time would have seemed a blessed relief, otherwise I would not have taken the risk that the hospital staff were not prepared to take on my behalf. Even so, my Nightingale training about the administration of drugs to patients and their strict regulations still lived powerfully within me. The next morning I looked with a refreshed but guilty gaze into the eyes of the night nurse—who brightly remarked that she had known I would sleep anyway.

My second misdemeanour came after I had been in the hospital for about two weeks and had settled down to a pleasant and progressive, if still frail, existence in the single ward. One day, the main ward was buzzing with admissions and my little ward was needed for a sicker person. They sent my favourite nurse in to break the news to me, which she did with her customary sweetness.

This news I greeted with a sense of shock. It seemed, without my realising it, illness had made me deeply insecure. All my security had been shut up with me in that little room. To abandon it was something I would not do lightly. The whole fabric of the room, its wall marks, its corners, all its little shapes and characters had become part of myself. I remember the day I had taken my first shaky steps, when my numerous attachments and tubes had been removed, and managing to reach the window. And how the view of the reservoirs in Barnes had been part of a soaring achievement. That lovely view. No, I decided, I would not go without a fuss. When you are as weak as I was then, anything that touches your emotions, touches them profoundly.

I did go, however. After my pathetic objections began to sound hollow even to myself, my belongings were heaped onto my bed I was moved back to the ward of four people where I had been before. Doris was still there, full of her histoires and scoring-off the ancillary workers. She hated the upheaval of floor polishing but she was quite glad to see me back.

A third failing on my part came in my relations with the physiotherapist. A kinder, more cheerful woman it would have been hard to find—brightly and breezily she daily greeted my long-drawn face. I did not welcome her not only because it was a substantial interruption that I resented, but because she made me do breathing exercises that were a considerable effort and which hurt me. All the nursing and medical treatments I had accepted automatically, even when they were painful, but those breathing exercises became a daily grind I dreaded. Of course, it was necessary and I did it, but never with good grace. However, I had reason later to be grateful for her kindness. The locum physiotherapists who appeared at weekends had much less patience, and rolled me around and thumped my back as though they were making dough. As long as I managed to cough up something they had their reward. After one particularly severe drumming from a herculean woman with not much time to spare, I was reduced to mute fragility for hours. If I needed putting in my place, she did it.

However, what seemed to me by far my worst misdemeanour came at the very beginning of my period in 8th South. My only excuse can be that I was still very ill. As everyone knows who has been in a hospital, the last event of the night is the drugs round. Owing to my position in the ward, I was last but one of the twenty six patients. Sometimes I had to wait till 11 p.m. until that trolley came my way. By which time the searing hours of the day had tiredness, like flames about my back. My various conditions meant that movement was very difficult. I was trapped for long periods in one or another position that all the lambswool rugs, rubber rings, rubbings and attention could not make comfortable for long. Therefore, by the late evening, exhaustion was ripping holes in my normal reluctance to complain. One evening I remember crying out for the round to be finished and the lights out. On the third night of this purgatory, I begged the night nurse to start the drug round at our end of the ward the following night. But to ask such a service is impossible—drug rounds always seem to be done clockwise.

Obviously the impression I had made on the nurse was not a favourable one. I heard her say in exasperation to her assistant nurse, 'These Nightingales seem to think they are...'

The end of the sentence faded into other environs of the ward. I was left not knowing what it is that Nightingales think of themselves. Did we think we were gods? What was it we thought we were? I shall never know now. All I knew then was that I was no Nightingale. Just a patient, uncomfortable, feeble, miserable and longing for the day to end.

20

Since my illnesses in the Charing Cross, I have had plenty of time for reflection about what that nurse said. Did Nightingales think they were special? Were we thought of as some sort of nursing elite that other nurses disliked? I suppose we did think the Nightingale Training was the best. (Not all, of course—some found it very oppressive.) But then most people who have been to a London teaching hospital think their training is the best. Get a few nurses or medicos together, and the alma mater of each is ideal. But, I suppose, there were aspects about Nightingales that were different.

The first, of course, was our name. We were the only nurses to be trained in the original nurses training school started by Florence Nightingale and the only ones to bear her name. And what a lovely name it is. One cannot imagine a prettier name to be called. Supposing Florence Nightingale had been called Florence Baker or Florence Wrightson. Well, those might have been appropriate names for a training school—the Baker Training School or the Wrightson Training School. But Bakers and Wrightsons wouldn't have sounded like nurses at all. Nightingale is one of the most elegant names a nurse could hope to have.

The Nightingale badge is special too. Compared with the very ordinary S.R.N. badges, the Nightingale badge could be a medal of state. Beautifully shaded in an alloy of silvery metals to form a cross, the prongs of which are swallow tailed and covered in purple enamel. There is a fleur-de-lys in its north west and south east angles. The Rose of England in the south west. And, in the north east, the coat-of-arms of the City of London. The central disc shows a relief of Miss Nightingale's right profile.

On the back of my badge is inscribed my name and the date of the year I completed my training. Underneath, the single word, 'Loyalty'. Have I been loyal? With my hand on my heart, I think I have.

Then there was the position of the hospital itself. Beautiful siting of buildings inevitably improves their stature and St Thomas's has a position on the Thames that must be second to none. The coiling vistas of the Thames, and the oatmeal spires of the Houses of Parliament, stirred in me feelings of pride and sharpened my senses. They gave the building its own dreams of majesty and—in a part of London where there is a dearth of open spaces—all that is necessary to escape the madding crowd.

As for the Nightingale Training itself, of that I have already given much evidence of its excellence. A recent meeting with Peggy confirmed that it had not changed. She and I met for an animated reunion at the Hot Pot at Peter Jones, our old stamping ground. We had kept in touch over the years but, she with her three children and I with my two, had been kept busy enough for our meetings to be rare. Christmas cards had been exchanged; telephones calls were commonplace. But, since we had left St Thomas's, we had only met on a few occasions and this was to be the last time.

I, who had just recovered from my serious illness, did not realise that she was about to get her even more serious illness—from which she since has died, A blow which I still cannot come to terms with and which she, herself, faced with such characteristic courage. But that day at Peter Jones—that glorious day—I was recovered and she was not yet ill. And we sat for five hours chatting about the past.

She had not changed at all except, perhaps, for a little more weight around her middle. Her style, her laugh, her gaiety were still on the surface or just underneath. She was thrilled to hear that I was writing a book about our training and filled in some gaps for me.

'Do you remember writing messages on the backs of our hands or inside corners of our aprons? ' she asked.

How it all came flooding back.

'Do you still put your pillow case openings away from the door?' she wondered.

'I think I do, but not consciously.'

'No, but our training got at the subconscious don't you think?'

I pondered. 'Yes, I think it did. But most things get at my subconscious.'

We laughed like we used to do. Then we went on talking for hours over our patés and bitter lemons.

'I hope you write like you talk,' she said.

I told her some of the things I had written about. Her eyes magnified and eyebrows flew into her forehead. 'Heavens, Sue, I wouldn't have dared put that.' She started to reminisce about Beatrice Ward. 'Do you know Sister Beatrice always talked to my cap?'

'I think I remember that from when she was Night Sister. But I preferred it that way. It spared me some of the guilt I should have been feeling.'

'I didn't like the night rounds',' rejoined Peggy. 'I dreaded them. You know that Nurse… passed out stone cold before a night round.'

'She didn't!' I exclaimed, mentally making a note. 'Well, I'm not surprised. It was like waiting for the Gestapo to drop in. All those names to remember. My memory for names was never my strong point.'

'Nor mine,' said Peggy.

'It's just as well we are not training now,' I said. 'My memory for names has almost gone.

Our lunch passed to tea and we ordered again to continue our conversation. That day was a consolidation of all the happiest times we spent together. Had I not decided to write this book, we would never have had that precious last day together, the bill for which Peggy insisted on paying.

Just before we left, as Peter Jones was closing its doors and a waitress hustled us from our seats, Peggy told me that she knew a nursing sister who had worked in many teaching hospitals round the world, but still considered the Nightingale training unique.

So it hadn't changed.

I decided to go back to the hospital to explore and try to assess with eyes that had grown thirty years older, what had changed, and whether I could still recapture that strange, inexplicable power it had had over me, and the affection I had felt for it.

The new buildings I had seen from a distance on numerous occasions. I can remember quite clearly, too, the plans for those buildings which we, as nurses, had impassively regarded in matron's office in 1953. The original designs for the modern hospital had effectively wiped out all the old Henry Currey blocks that we knew. Replacing them with three lumpy blocks on the river front and an assortment of others behind. The conservationists, however, stretched themselves—shortage of funds interceded as well—and the results are now there for all to see.

I found the approach from Westminster Bridge quite an impressive one, with its fountain playing multi-giro shapes amid lawns and shrubs. Ahead of me the massive north wing, with its rather plain dressings, hid from that angle any sight of the buildings that I had known but I was happy to see the well beloved statues lined up to greet me. The emporium of the ground floor of the new wing where I could buy my flowers, my stationery, make my enquiries and have a cup of tea and a sausage roll, led into the corridor that I had known so well.

On entering the corridor, shock and amazement hit me. It seemed to have become so narrow. Where had its width, its height, its distinction gone? Finding that places have withered and shrunk and become like toys compared with my memories of them in childhood, were such frequent experiences, it was as though my life at St Thomas's had been transposed to my childhood and I had since grown up.. It was not until I had walked right to the end of the corridor that I found part of the reason for this.

There, between the last two blocks, remained the distinctive windows that had given the corridor its character and light, with their soaring height, their twelve panes and their fanlight tops. Nearly all the others had been blocked in or destroyed. Only in that one section, the corridor appeared to broaden out again and breathe the essence of its bygone days. I recalled walking along that corridor at night and the diagonal shafts of moonlight through which I had trodden, and realised that there would not be many moonbeams now.

Back in the main hall, I was aware, too, of a sense of loss. That hall—once the main entrance to the hospital and its focal point in many ways—was now robbed of its light and door. The pillars, arches and busts that surrounded it looked lost, as in some antechamber of a museum. Even the massive statue of Queen Victoria had been moved to one side, its image deflated in what seemed like an annexe to its former central position. From the hall I walked up the main stairway onto the first floor. The chapel was still there and appeared quite unchanged. The names on the tablets at either side of the altar, of medical and nursing staff who had worked and died there, struck several painful chords. Surely not him—he seemed such a very young man.

I moved out of the chapel and along the first floor and it was unrecognizable in some ways. Vanished windows, little snuggeries for staff in unidentifiable slots, departments had appeared, as if from nowhere, in rooms that either did not exist or of whose existence I had been quite unaware. The cohesion and, perhaps, simplicity of its former days had gone. I peered into some of the first floor wards where I had worked. For some the oak strip flooring had gone and there were smart, shining vinyl squares. Apart from that and all the bed curtaining, they looked, from a distance, quite unchanged. Outside each ward a notice declared the visiting times in no uncertain terms. They still seemed less liberal than in other hospitals. Good for them.

The lifts beside them looked quite different now. The old fashioned lifts shafts had been sealed in so that the stone stairs that wound round them had no dimensions any more. I thought to myself, there would he no opportunity to spot matron now on a lower floor—and collision might have occurred. I noticed, too, that the staff were using the lifts, which had never been allowed in our day.

Old habits die hard, so I walked up the stairs to the second floor. From the staircase I had a bird's-eye view of all the clutter of buildings, the immense pipes and all the other necessities, though intrusions, that now filled what had once been the lawns and paving stones of Currey's original hospital. Nostalgia seemed to fill my legs with lead. Had I been blind when I worked there, or had it changed less than I thought?

From there I went outside to inspect what I could from the front. At that stage it was not possible to wander along the terrace, and what remained of the colonnade was sealed up anyway. From the Embankment, the hospital appeared to have aged a thousand years. Great warts of wooden huts stared out of windowed eyes above the remains of the colonnade where the balustrade had once so proudly sat. The balustrade, in places, still existed. But broken and torn, like ancient remains that hundreds of years of weathering had reduced to rubble. At the front of the colonnade, the inscription of the first stone laid still existed. To the left of the remaining wall that had been the foundation of the block containing the old Florence, Charity and Christian Wards, wild flowers grew in colourful profusion on the bank.

So much for its appearance I went back inside to see if there were any way I could feel if its spirit had changed. Certainly the volume of human traffic was the same. Nursing and medical start flew around at tangents. The nursing uniform was simpler, still striped but less bulk, weight and length. But of the belts I could find no link with the past. A less distinctive imitation of our Nightingale caps still existed, I was happy to see. Although there were, too, plenty of the cottage hospital caps I had heard about.

The nurses all looked bright and happy but features seem to change mysteriously with generations; they did not look like us. One of them came up to me and most kindly asked if she could direct me anywhere. I found myself dumb and inarticulate. She gave me a sweet smile and passed along.

But then, coming along the corridor, there was a sister. Still with that special aura of comfort and control and her uniform not changed at all. How good it was to see. To me, the sisters were the integral soul of St Thomas's. I don't think I realised how much till I saw one again. And then, there was a charge nurse, too, also in the same style of uniform—with benevolence and confidence locked into a purposeful expression as she sped to her destination. After that I began to relax—its heart and its core were still the same. What else?

The medical staff boomed around the corridors. I heard much deep laughter, as I looked for the place where matron's office had once been. White coats were fanning out as jokes punctuated the air in their slipstreams. Confidence was everywhere, or so it seemed. Some fellows I noticed were going into the nurses' dining room. That was a change. I went to investigate and was nearly knocked over by a sign saying 'Staff Only'. But, from what I could see, it did not appear to have changed.

Echoes from the past, too, came from all the many familiar names of new wards, departments and lecture halls—Nevin, Wrigley, Evan Jones, Bowes, Garland, Gullan. And City Ward still remained. I crept up past sister's old room and peeped into it, as ghosts of memories formed before my eyes and filled my ears. Dear City of London Ward—how could you ever change?

Once I had satisfied myself about City, I had had my fill. I had not come to venture into all the new parts of the hospital that had not been part of our era. There was no point in that. I had come to see what was left of our time in the fifties. I had found some of it and lost some of it. But the pride remained and that pride is sealed in time.